I Can Explain Everything:

CONFESSIONS OF
A PET CAPYBARA

by
Dobby the Capybara
&
Stacy Winnick

Illustrated by Sonya Reasor

Published by Bratty Capybara Press

Published in the United States of America

Book designed by Sonya Reasor.
Cover by Sonya Reasor.
sonyareasor.com / sonyaseattle@gmail.com

Effect of Climate Change on Hydrochoerus hydrochaeris, The Theft, My Front Teeth, and *The Quiz* were previously published at Dobby the Capybara (website). They have been re-formatted to fit your television screen.

First Printing September 2017

ISBN 978-0-9993976-0-2 (Paperback Edition)
ISBN 978-0-9993976-1-9 (eBook Edition)
Library of Congress Control Number 2017913859

Printed on planet earth

Visit www.petcapybara.com

For information about special discounts available for bulk purchases, sales promotions, fund-raising and educational needs, please contact the author through the website contact forms.

To my brother,
Caplin Rous,
The World's Most Famous Capybara
July 10, 2007 to January 4, 2011

CONTENTS

Chapter One

Anatomy of a Capybara

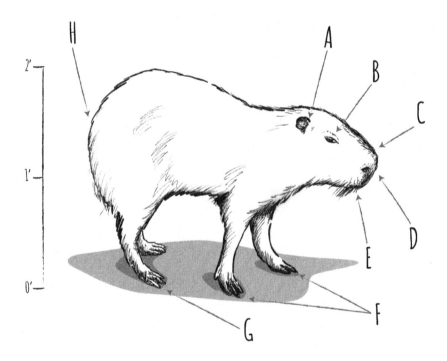

A—ear, B—eyeball, C—morrillo, D—schnozzola, E— mouth, F—front feet (4 toes), G—back feet (3 toes), H—no tail here

WHAT IS A CAPYBARA?

Everybody's first question is "What in the heck is that?" I've even heard a ruder version of that question when a Bible salesman spotted me in the front yard. To respond to the folks who are asking, simply uttering "capybara" is completely meaningless. In a hurry to please, people usually perk up and offer the only tidbit of data their puny human minds can dredge up: "From Australia, right?" Young humans seem to be better educated and much politer than the geezers. Kids walk right up to pet me and ask a million questions, hardly waiting for the ever-present Farm Manager to answer. If only I had vocal chords! The "Australia, right?" people hang back, insisting that I am from Australia—well okay, maybe it is New Zealand—while the Farm Manager's smile purses down into a bite-your-tongue mask of tolerance. That's when she gives up and pulls my favorite treat out of her big coat pocket: corn on the cob. I can bite a frightening chunk out of that corn, right through the husk to the cob, a moon-sized crater, and corn juice flows like lava from my mouth.

Unfortunately, you're not looking at me in person, so I put lots of pictures in this book. I'm much bigger than these pictures, though. Try to imagine a potato shaped dog with short legs, a shoebox head, and fur like a coconut. Don't forget the teeth! I have much bigger teeth than a beaver, because they are only the second largest rodent. Or you could picture a cute little guinea pig, a very close relative. Select the basic brown model (we don't come in colors yet) and blow it up as big as a German shepherd dog, and add slightly webbed feet. Let's try again. How about a hippopotamus with fur like broom straw, skinny legs, get rid of the tail nonsense, but keep the submerged-in-water part, and you definitely want to keep the wiggly ears. The basic idea is that I'm big, I'm chunky, and I can take big bites out of things.

Here's another thing that I'm not: a nutria! Lots of people claim to have seen capybaras "around." No, they have seen nutrias. Nutrias, or Coypu, are about tomcat size, brown with a big long ratty tail and persimmon orange teeth. Very cute, but an introduced nuisance everybody now regrets. They swim around, dig holes, eat everything in sight, and wreck the wetlands. Then our smaller, less destructive muskrats end up leaving town. Speaking of beavers, I'm not one of those, either, but it's hard to miss the tail difference. Plus, I'm more than twice as big as a beaver, neatly holding down our claim of World's Largest Rodent.

Capybaras come from South America, slogging through the squishy grasslands of every country but Chile. Even though we can swim, none of us live "north"

2

of the Panama Canal. (It's actually west, check a map!) A few of us got stuck in Panama, between the canal and the mountains to the south. They are a lot smaller than me, and those poor little guys are endangered. Their habitat got kinda chopped up, so they are stuck in smaller, disconnected areas and have to sneak back and forth between a lot of smaller soggy areas. We big capys are quite common, and in some countries we are ranched and (shudders) eaten. Long ago, a regrettably misinformed pope declared us to be a fish, and we are now a Lenten delicacy. (Takes out a notebook, writes letter to pope asking for reversal of ridiculous fish designation, checks email, and continues.) I keep waiting to hear that all of the capybaras in South America are relocating to Brazil, where we are appreciated and protected.

Capybaras live throughout the warmer soggy bits of South America[1]. There are millions of us out in the boondocks like the Pantanal, a seasonally flooded chunk of Brazil, Bolivia, and Paraguay that's as big as Washington State. There are millions of us on the plateaus and up in the mountains, always sticking close to a river or lake. There are even millions of us in small towns and big cities, even Rio de Janeiro! Well, it seems like millions, because we make a pest of ourselves when we get into town. Anyway, we're not endangered. Our habitat is endangered, though. That's why we come into town for kicks so often.

---

1   But not Chile. We never made it over the Andes.

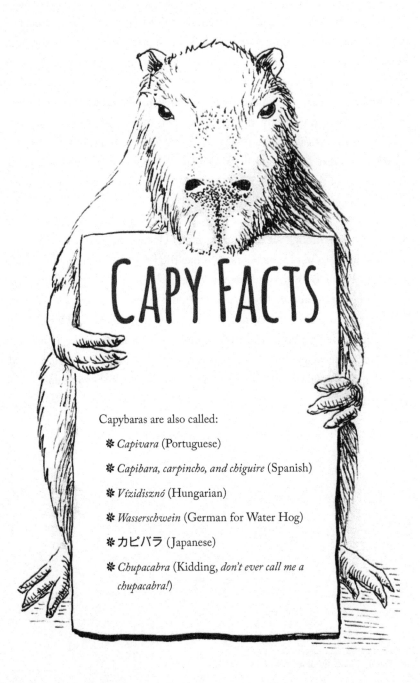

Capybaras are also called:

❋ *Capivara* (Portuguese)

❋ *Capibara, carpincho, and chiguire* (Spanish)

❋ *Vízidisznó* (Hungarian)

❋ *Wasserschwein* (German for Water Hog)

❋ カピバラ (Japanese)

❋ *Chupacabra* (Kidding, *don't ever call me a chupacabra!*)

So, we're common, but not always seen, like North American deer. Big and sneaky. We graze and browse and farmers don't like to see us among their crops. If you ask a South American to show you a capybara ("Oh yes, they are everywhere!") it is like asking a North American to show you a deer. Common, yes, but elusive, yes indeedy. We are vegetarians, very shy and flighty, and hang around in herds, taking turns looking out for trouble. Daytime, country capybaras nap in the open and graze whenever, while in cities we hide out during the day, emerging at dusk to graze all night. Like deer, we are very adaptable, leaving the new developments, slipping back in to the older established towns. We're all over the roads, too, and like deer, we can really mess up your car. North Americans love their deer, right? Try to find a deer souvenir. It's the same with capybaras in South America: beloved, common, but go ahead and look for a t-shirt or ashtray. (Note: marketing opportunity.)

Authentic wild capybaras lazing about in some leech-infested river

Capybaras aren't usually found in South American suburbs, though we do sneak into swimming pools once in a while. We are wetland animals, and in the wild we spend half the day in water, pretending we are safe. When we are stuffed full of juicy water plants, we mosey on up to the grassy areas near the edge of the water. Mostly, we graze, so picture a herd of short, chubby, horse-faced deer, munching away. We also stand around a lot. If you decide to check us out at a zoo, don't expect a dynamic display with lots of running around. We aren't simply cooperating with the paparazzi: we are wary. We are fearful, and we monitor everything with our 359° vision, because we are a prey animal. We are the hunted, not the hunter, and we spook easily because that's what survival is all about, down here at the bottom of the food chain.

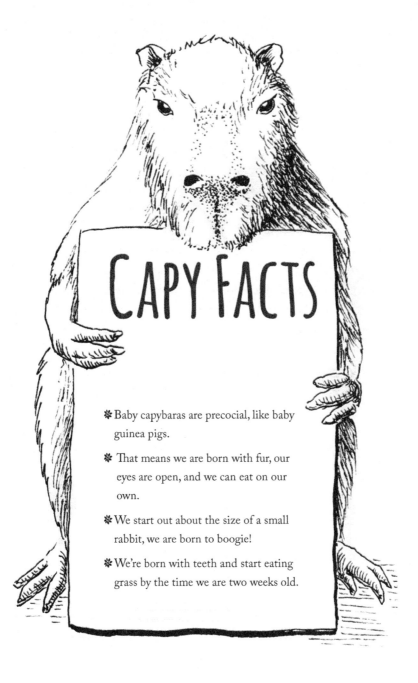

CAPY FACTS

❊ Baby capybaras are precocial, like baby guinea pigs.

❊ That means we are born with fur, our eyes are open, and we can eat on our own.

❊ We start out about the size of a small rabbit, we are born to boogie!

❊ We're born with teeth and start eating grass by the time we are two weeks old.

Ugh, predators. I think that is the real coup for capybaras who are born in the USA. Our main predators are pretty much not living here, though there are some wild stories coming out of Florida. Jaguars are a Very Big Deal in South America. You might think that being semi-aquatic would be a huge advantage, but darned if those suckers don't swim! We can leap right off the bank of the river—we pretty much stay within ½ mile of serious water—and that Jaguar can jump in right after us! Our big-boy skin is nearly Jaguar-proof, but the babies are at a distinct disadvantage. That's not all, though. Anacondas are great huge snakes that swallow us alive! And they swim, too. The gigantic Harpy Eagles snatch up our little guys, and caiman, crocodiles, boa constrictors, foxes, ocelots, vultures, and the dramatic crested caracaras consider the wee tiny ones to be gourmet treats. Don't even ask me about the electric eels and piranhas! None of those are found in the Pacific Northwest, I am happy to report. Feral dogs are a big problem in the wild, and dogs here can be scary if they appear suddenly with the barking engaged without a "kill" button. The absolute scariest thing in the suburbs, though, is the little girls squealing and shrieking on that trampoline next door, talking heads popping up above the top of the fence. Absolutely terrifying!

The mighty capybara leaps to the safety of the Amazon from the riverbank

You see, it isn't all that bad living in the suburbs. I live in a wetland. I have a mini-pond and a spring-fed creek. The Farm Manager tells me there is another pond in our basement but I have never seen it. She has bought me SIX swimming pools! One by one, I destroyed or rejected them all. Except the latest one. It's a beauty. I have my own fancy bed, all heated, safe, and cozy. Nothing sneaks up on me at night. Three hot meals a day, served in the kitchen, very proper. Snacks, laundry service, private bath, a hot tub and spa, The Chambermaid straightens up several times a day. I keep thinking I'm going to have to sell my soul to pay the bill. Eight years have passed, and I have never seen an invoice.

There's one more fact we need to get straight before I start telling whoppers. I am not a domestic animal. I am a tame wild animal. Domestication is a complicated process that occurs between humans and animals over thousands of years. Consider how long it took cave men to turn wolves into dachshunds! My grandparents, my parents, and I were all born here in the USA but that's not enough time to make us domestic. I think it is going to be very cool when you can buy CapyChow at the grocery store. The best improvement will be when we come in different colors. Giraffe is very popular right now, and that is a vastly underutilized pattern in the animal world. I can do without the ridiculous neck though, with these stubby legs. Let's be realistic.

THE ADVENTURE BEGINS

All visitors eventually ask the Farm Manager "Why did you get a capybara?" Okay, I am standing right next to her, in all my glory, a magnificent creature, right? Still, they turn to the Farm Manager and ask her why she got me! As if I'm not listening, or not paying attention to anything but the extra corn-on-the-cob that sits on the kitchen counter when visitors arrive. Why indeed? To know me is to love me, right? She saw me, checked me over, compared me to my rambunctious and rather unfriendly, not to mention unsanitary, siblings. Now that you mention it, I don't know why she was in Texas right then, but seriously, anyone would have brought me home.

Good guess, I was born in Texas. Nobody snatched me from the rainforests of Australia. My parents and grandparents were all born in Arkansas, but where we came from before that is rather fuzzy. Pet capybaras were as common as hen's teeth back then, so for many long and insignificant years, the Farm Manager was stuck with mini-rodents like gerbils and chinchillas. She started out with one boring old brown hamster when she was learning to walk. To help keep her balance, she dragged that sorry hamster in his cage all around the apartment, but that is her story, not mine. Having perfected "tiny," for she is a puny little human, she fantasized about giant rodents like beavers and porcupines. After discovering the world-renowned and probably the very first book about pet capybaras, *Capyboppy*[2], only the magnificent and most humongous rodent would do.

In addition to the unmitigated thrill of a giant rat in the kitchen, there are the free lawn mowing services, the near perfect security system, and the proper use for that neglected swimming pool. She dreamed about capybaras day and night, and once the Internet was invented, it was only a matter of time before live baby capybaras became available. Breeders would ship an adult capybara in 2008, throwing some potatoes into the shipping container for food and water. Most breeders declined to ship little babies, though, so the Farm Manager eventually gave in and picked me up in person. I'll tell you what I can remember about it.

---

2   *Capyboppy* is a 1966 book about a pet capybara by Bill Peet. You have to buy that book, too.

Capy Facts

❀ Surprise! There is a video to watch![3]

❀ I was only two weeks old, and had my
first visitors!

❀ I'm the baby that everybody is holding,
but I didn't go home with them.

Caplin Rous was the World's Most Famous Capybara. He also happened to be my big brother. We had the same parents, but I was born two litters later. Caplin came home to visit his parents when I was two weeks old. (There is a video of our meeting![3]) Why didn't my big brother take me home to live with him? Okay, Caplin was a bit surly, and he even clicked at me, never a good sign. Clicking[4] is like squirrel chatter, meaning Caplin was not impressed and maybe even wanted to bite me. What about those people with him? They picked me up and carried me around like a prize pig, but left me behind when they drove away. They visited me a few years later, but they didn't try to take me home then, either.

Anyway, one week after this significant but unfruitful visit, the Farm Manager showed up. She didn't click at me or anything. Like the other people, she picked me up and kissed my nose. I was the smallest baby of the litter, but not a runt. I liked being held because my first humans had been bottle feeding me a milk supplement. People meant extra milk, so I eagerly hopped into the arms of any human. Pretending that she was being fair, the Farm Manager held me and observed my panicking siblings who darted around the pen like three wild boar piglets. She set me down and tackled the slowest beastlet and started to look it over when it nipped her on the tender inside of the elbow. She abruptly held the biter away as it let loose with an impressive shower of urine. Now that her clothes were soaked with Eau de Capybara, it was suddenly time to leave. She picked me back up, holding me tight, talking and talking to my human parents. They flipped me onto my back and looked at my nether regions, and everybody agreed that I was a boy. Duh, they could have asked. They placed me into a tiny crate and tossed in my first traveling potato. (It's the very same carrier the Farm Manager now uses for guinea pigs!) The Farm Manager carried me to a noisy smelly contraption. She slid onto the seat and set my tiny cage on her lap. There was a Driver human who sat in a special chair to our left with a wheel toy. The driver pushed and twisted things, the car made noises and started bumping around and I fell asleep.

---

3   Proof I met my brother Caplin! *Caplin Rous in Meet the Parents:* https://youtu.be/cN2lwakFxDs
4   Clicking is the most serious warning a capybara will give immediately before it attacks you. You don't want to stand around wondering what to do. My best advice is to grab a five-gallon bucket to use as a shield and back out of there. In the video I was very happy to have a fence between us because at two weeks old, we hadn't been issued our protective shields yet.

If you have a bottle of milk, you are my best friend.

The car suddenly quieted and I woke up. The Farm Manager hopped out of the car and shuffled me and my potato into a dry bathtub spread with a pristine white towel. That first night I was scared to eat anything except grass but the milk was good, and I hardly noticed how many different humans took turns holding the bottle. When the lights went out I realized that my potato and I would be sleeping right there, in Bathtub #1, and not returning to my familiar pen and siblings.

Bathtub #1 turned out to be kind of a capybara B&B, because in the morning, after my milk, the Farm Manager plunked me back into the tiny crate. She dropped in the rest of the grass and my potato and latched the cage door. Outside we went to the car which had filled with boxes. Once again we were settled onto the Farm Manager's lap, the Driver poked things to make the car roar and tremble, then played with the wheel for a while. When we arrived at the world's noisiest and smelliest place imaginable, the Driver stopped the car. Everyone quickly exited the car, the Driver unloaded the boxes to the sidewalk. She turned to the Farm Manager, hugged her, and jumped back in. The car door clunked shut, it roared and lumbered away.

The Farm Manager juggled the boxes into a maneuverable upright tower and balanced my cage on top. We trundled toward the doors of a stark but stinky building and the Farm Manager talked to a bunch of people who took most of the boxes away. Next, the Farm Manager talked to a uniformed man for a while.

"No, it's not from Australia."

"Yes, that is his bottle and the white powder is his milk. Per airline regulations, I have 24 hours' worth of food affixed to his travel crate, he's a baby and milk is his food."

"No, that is not a hand grenade, it is a potato."

My potato knows all.

Suddenly another man in khakis whisked me and my potato away from the Farm Manager. I wish I could tell you that they took me to the cockpit and I got to fly the plane that day. Instead, they crammed my travel carrier into the belly of the plane where it stank like a million dogs.

Hours later, more uniformed men lifted my little crate out of the frying pan and dumped it into the fire. I wish that was true because it would have been better than what really came next. They yanked my tiny cage out of the doggy dark place and set it onto an open-air version of a car and forgot about me. This could have been a good thing, but suddenly my nostrils were attacked by frozen air, and this time all smells stopped. Cold crept onto my skin and hair and eyeballs. My potato and I spent an eternity freezing outdoors and then my little cage soared and swung around and I heard the Farm Manager talking to me again! She freed me from my cage, held me tight and warmed me up. Instead of giving me a bottle of milk, though, she nervously juggled her boxes into another tower and quickly steered us back into the freezing cold. We passed a million cars, finally stopping at a car that smelled like chicken feed and duck doodoo. The Farm Manager unceremoniously tossed the shamble of boxes into the back of the car. She transformed into a Driver with her own toy wheel. She secured my crate, poked and twisted some buttons and rumbled away. As the car heated to a balmy tropical paradise, my potato and I fell asleep in my tiny cage. I awoke in the biggest, most glorious bathtub I had ever seen! Best of all, there was milk!

What is it about bathtubs, anyway? Bathtub #2 was a heart-shaped cistern, big enough to hold four sixth graders or maybe a duck recuperating from surgery. Now it was stuffed with blankets, a heat lamp, food and water, a potty bowl, a stuffed rabbit, a super-sized Eggo waffle box upcycled as a capy-cave, and my potato. The decor was so-so, and anyway I learned how to jump out about a week later. Most of the day I hung around with the Farm Manager in the middle of the house: the kitchen. Kitchens are the best. Mine provided a steady supply of food (potatoes!) and water, another heat lamp, and a very attractive basket with a blue pillow that was perfect for naps.

I have my own refrigerator, now. It's downstairs, not far from the underground pond. When I was a baby, I shared the kitchen refrigerator with the Farm Manager and The Bartender. He is a human I share everything with, including the Farm Manager. The Bartender quickly learned how to open the refrigerator and whip up a bottle of milk, so he's become extremely useful. Everyone should have a bartender on staff.

The daily routine was nearly ideal. The Farm Manager fed me a bottle of milk every morning. Hay, potatoes, vegetables, and fruit abounded. I ate almost anything, even guinea pig pellets, Cheerios,™ Kix,™ shredded wheat, and the Farm Manager's hair. A second bottle appeared magically at noon, and in the afternoon, and again at dinnertime, and even another one right before bed. *Five times a day!* Currently, I have been cut back to two and a half milks a day, because nobody loves me anymore. Surely an eight-year-old capybara that weighs twenty-five times what a baby weighs needs *more milk,* not less! This is the kind of backwards Farm Manager thinking that drives me crazy.

Wild capybaras spend half their day in water, but that doesn't begin to explain why captive baby capybaras automatically use potty bowls. We just do, and that's a fact, Jack. It's convenient and endearing, but ultimately misleading. Some captive full grown capybaras continue to use a tub of water, unlike wild adults who decorate the nearby river banks. My own adult deposits create an attention-getting statement unparalleled by any other utterance I am capable of. I would not now squander them in a bowl.

Like all baby capybaras, I properly used my potty bowl on sight. A shallow bowl on the floor, an inch of water, and we all poop and pee in it, without any training. It can go downhill from there, but Baby Me was a little angel. All baby capybaras are, and that's how the fantasy begins. There was no potty bowl in the kitchen, though. The Chambermaid[5] placed mine in the shower stall adjacent to Bathtub #2 to make cleanup easy. I was meticulous with my poopies and The Chambermaid became proficient at lifting the floppy rubber bowl to the toilet. It's an ideal setup for a good little capybara that weighs about five pounds. It's not at all ideal for a naughty boy who weighs over one hundred pounds and learns to grab the bowl with my chompers and toss it! Remember that when you get to the part about habitat loss.

Baby Me could be trusted to scamper up the stairs to that shower stall, do my business, wipe my feet on the carpet, and rejoin the family activities. There were no accidents in the kitchen when I was a baby. This is how angelic and naive baby capybaras are. Baby Me was a paragon of innocence.

---

5   The Farm Manager is also The Chambermaid, but I want it to sound like I employ a large staff.

Grazing in the wintery back yard was unpleasant. The Farm Manager hovered over me like a noisy obnoxious protective shield, scanning the sky for hawks and crows, comparing my diminutive size with dozens of hidey holes and garden crevices. The ducks towered over me, trundling past like a herd gone berserk, while the hens scratched up dirt into my face. Even the rabbits were twice my size, competing for the same sparse stands of winter grass. The kitchen was warm and dry, and fresh grass magically appeared in my bowl, as if conjured up offsite. My early requirements as a prince were not yet well defined, but I was catching on.

The first days at home with the Farm Manager were all about me. I was the center of the universe, whether I was drinking milk from a bottle, exploring the Funny Farm, or napping at someone's feet. At my first veterinary checkup, Dr. F pronounced me eminently more suitable as a pet than the savage sugar gliders he had examined the day before. I did not devour a finger, which is what he had assumed I would do. I was such a good little capy, napping and drinking my milk. And then the Farm Manager started disappearing during the day. She had a job to do and it wasn't about me.

Here's the thing. I like The Bartender, I really do, but I am resentful of anyone who attempts to oust the Farm Manager. And he made many assumptions those first days when the Farm Manager started her periodic disappearances. First, he assumed that I would accept him as a surrogate, simply because he gave me milk at the correct times. Second, he assumed I would behave myself and be content to hang out in Bathtub #2 all day long. Third, he assumed that I was healthy. And so did everyone else.

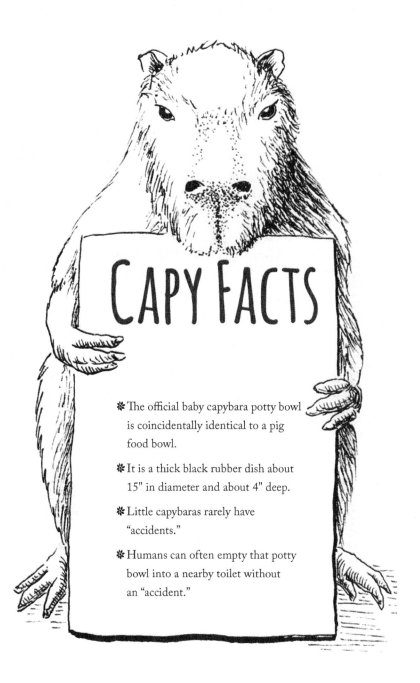

CAPY FACTS

❋ The official baby capybara potty bowl is coincidentally identical to a pig food bowl.

❋ It is a thick black rubber dish about 15" in diameter and about 4" deep.

❋ Little capybaras rarely have "accidents."

❋ Humans can often empty that potty bowl into a nearby toilet without an "accident."

THE FIRST TIME I ALMOST DIED

Do you remember when I talked earlier about being really, really cold after my big stinky coming home experience? Maybe that cold was a coincidence, but about ten days after my first veterinary checkup, I suddenly revisited Dr. F. Capybaras are supposed to make cute little *eep*ing noises, but I didn't. I checked out my environment, but I wasn't as curious as a puppy or kitten. Most baby animals are rambunctious, veering from crazy antics to deathlike intensity naps throughout the day. Shouldn't I be playful? Why didn't I make any cute baby sounds? Why wasn't I frisky?

The disappearing Farm Manager left The Bartender on his own to serve my milk. I was unusually tired, but a napping baby capybara is a good capybara, right? When the Farm Manager returned home that evening, the center of her universe, little Dobby, didn't come running. My potty bowl was still clean, and she correctly suspected I hadn't been in it that day. She gently set me into the potty bowl, where I collapsed and crumpled over onto my side! Good thing it was a clean bowl! She grabbed a towel and dried me off, but I was listless and floppy as a sock monkey. The veterinary clinic was closed for the evening, so I had to survive another 18 hours at home before any fixing-up could start.

Under-inflated

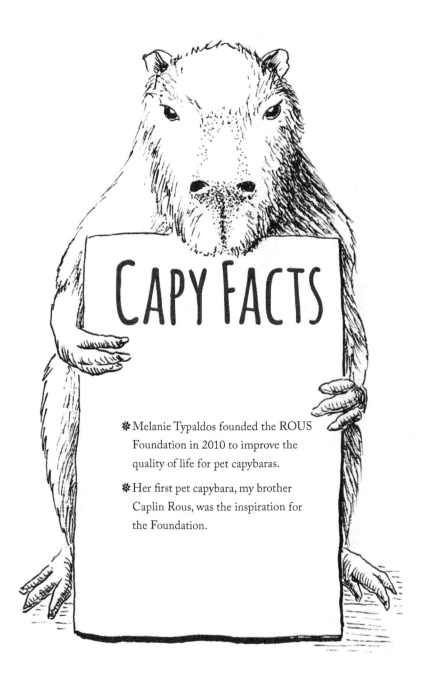

CAPY FACTS

* Melanie Typaldos founded the ROUS Foundation in 2010 to improve the quality of life for pet capybaras.

* Her first pet capybara, my brother Caplin Rous, was the inspiration for the Foundation.

The Farm Manager cuddled me up in a blanket to keep me warm and alert, and maybe to keep me from tipping over again. The calm demeanor of the days since my arrival now seemed a sinister premonition. The Farm Manager phoned the only capybara expert in the world, Miss Mary Lee in Arkansas. Despite the inconvenient time zone difference, to the famous capybara breeder this was not an unusual phone call. The Farm Manager, at first stunned by her distinguished Arkansas accent, told Miss Mary Lee that I had fallen face down into my poop bowl. To this day I can't believe what her prescription was. The Farm Manager thanked her, hung up the phone, and together they saved my puny life.

"Corn syrup." Miss Mary Lee had said, "give him corn syrup from a syringe, orally, 'til he perks up. And keep givin' it 'till you get 'im to the vet in the morning. And, good luck, sweetheart."

Corn syrup, really? High Fructose Corn Syrup (HFCS) is the most maligned substance on the face of the planet. Embarrassingly, the Farm Manager had a sticky old bottle hidden way in the back of the lowest kitchen cupboard. All the boxes and jars in front of it had to come out and the Farm Manager crawled on her belly like a lizard to reach for it, but there it was. Nobody had thrown it out. An ersatz Hanukah Miracle. That old bottle is probably worth something on eBay, but it lives forever on that shelf because it's magical.

We have millions of syringes around here because that's what the Farm Manager uses for giving medicine to birds and to feed sick guinea pigs. She loaded up a little one with corn syrup and plunged it into my mouth. The results were immediate and stunning. Have you ever seen the movie *Pulp Fiction?* If so, you know the scene, because you fell off your chair the first time you saw it. If not, let's say the corn syrup worked like a double espresso, or maybe a quadruple one. But then I almost fell into my milk a few minutes later, and so began the routine for the night: milk, corn syrup, collapse, milk, corn syrup, and repeat.

Not certain why I kept deflating, the Farm Manager treated me for a generic respiratory condition. Absent our defunct antique humidifier, she improvised by spending the night with me in Bathtub #2, the adjacent running shower creating a steam bath. As the Farm Manager considered how much easier her life would now be had she adopted a mangy old dog from the local shelter, I was fighting for my life, drinking bottle after bottle of milk, slurping up corn syrup, and picking through the non-stop fresh greens and fruit.

In the morning, the Farm Manager transformed herself into a Race Car Driver and we returned to the vet clinic in my tiny carrier. (It was super tight with both of us in there.) The diagnosis was pneumonia. No wonder I wasn't frisky and talkative! The syringes kept coming, but with real medicine now instead of corn syrup. I was feeling much better, but a week later the Farm Manager begrudgingly jammed me back into my tiny carrier for a follow-up visit. To show you how little she knows about veterinary care, Dr. F announced that the pneumonia was cleared up, but my liver was now involved. The syringes kept coming, but with liver medicine now instead of pneumonia medicine. By now everyone was freaking out. I did survive, of course. I started making typical baby capybara *Eeep!* sounds, started chewing things up, and showed off my baby version of the Doofus Dance[6]. I had lost a bunch of weight, though, and was baby-sized again. Everyone gave me non-stop attention, wondering if I would be stunted, or have long-term structural issues, or maybe continue to lose weight and become a hamster.

The Farm Manager's mom was famous for saying "You always worry about the wrong thing," but this time everybody's worrying was on target. In total, I had lost an entire month's worth of weight. It took me more than six months to catch up to an average capybara weight. I've been tested a couple times for liver function since then, and everything is a-okay now. I'm a great big capybara, and I am plenty obnoxious, so we figure I am all-systems-go now.

---

6   I'm going to explain Doofus Dancing in a couple pages, so hold your horses!

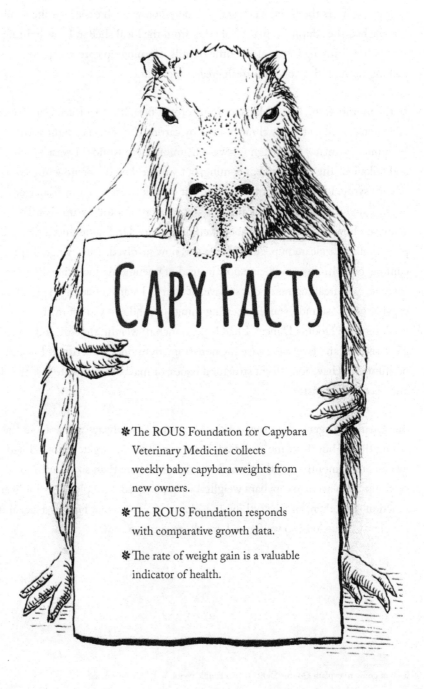

CAPY FACTS

❋ The ROUS Foundation for Capybara Veterinary Medicine collects weekly baby capybara weights from new owners.

❋ The ROUS Foundation responds with comparative growth data.

❋ The rate of weight gain is a valuable indicator of health.

MY ABBREVIATED CAREER

My big brother Caplin Rous, the World's Most Famous Capybara, went to work with his owner, Melanie, all the time. Caplin rode in the car, snuck in using the back stairs, slept on Melanie's desk at work, and rarely ate computer cables. In Seattle, lots of people take their dogs to work, and sometimes they behave. Everybody loves those mellow pups that sleep by your desk like a potted palm tree. Napping at work with the Farm Manager sounded much more fun than being abandoned every day!

My work day started with a scamper into my cat carrier. My big butt didn't fit in the tiny guinea pig one any more. The Farm Manager gathered up my potty bowl, a waterproof pad for under it, a towel, and a bucket for emptying and carrying the "water." Then there was my food: pellets, hay, vegetables and greens, powdered goat milk and baby oatmeal, bowls for everything and a water bowl large and heavy enough so I couldn't toss it. My white rabbit rug and a couple toys filled out the equipment bag. Whew!

Schlepping me and my equipment from the parking garage to the elevator, the Farm Manager whimpered slightly as she balanced my carrier on the top of the pile. Lurching backwards through the office door, she kicked everything into the office and watched to see the door latch shut. Ferrying my equipment past her stunned colleagues she immediately began to capybara-proof her office space. Wires were stashed behind barriers (also brought from home), plants were shoved up high so they wouldn't turn into lunch, important papers levitated or were filed. My equipment was meticulously arranged so that my exit from the potty bowl wouldn't be memorialized in carpet stains. A makeshift barrier appeared at her "door." Well, there was no door, it was a doorway, awkwardly wide. Between three and four boxes across, she stacked and jammed and crammed stuff in there like it was the Canadian border wall.

I was still shut in the cat carrier by the office door. Half a dozen strangers stooped down and peered through the airholes and shouted questions to the Farm Manager. She ignored them and they passed my carrier from one person to another, until someone set it back down and opened my door.

"Is it okay if we let it out?" someone said.

This got the Farm Manager's attention and she dropped her scissors, cardboard, and tape, and came running. For about ten minutes, she answered questions about me, deftly maneuvering past the Australian question quagmire. She droned on and on, watching closely as I explored the unsecured office areas, sniffing at shoelaces and computer cables, plants and wooden chair legs, stacks of books and manuals, anything I had been known to bite or chew. The office staff followed her gaze to the glass-walled conference room, their recently completed concept boards for tomorrow's presentation leaning against the wall.

"Excuse me," she said. "Can you help me keep this door closed today?" She sprinted to the conference room, sweeping me into her arms as the first board tipped over. The honeymoon was over.

While the Farm Manager shuffled papers at her desk I inspected the capybara proofing of her office. *Eep eep eep!* When capybaras wander any distance from their herd, we have little conversations, like cows mooing to each other. *Eep eep eeep!* It isn't very loud, but it can be strident. *Eep eep eeeep!* I sound like a Geiger counter, kind of a purr or trill. *Eep eep eeeeep!* If you have a pet guinea pig, you know the sound, except capybaras are quieter. It's strange that we are bigger but have wee little voices. *Eeep eep eeeeeep!* It's also a lot like a raccoon trill, if you are familiar with that. *Eeeeeeeeeeeeeeeep!*

"Okay, Dobby, what do you want?"

More milk!

See? It works every time. Okay, after about five times she would start to ignore me. When the Farm Manager started seriously working, I would leap that doorway barrier, or maybe shove my way through it, and explore the rest of the office! Nobody else had doors, either, and no one else put any barriers at all at their spaces! I would make the rounds, first asking for belly rubs and attention, then sniffing at shoelaces, computer cables, and books on the lower shelves. One by one they would shoo me away. I would wander back to the unattended storeroom for a while. When marking boxes in there got boring, I pulled some big papers down or knocked over some equipment to make the Farm Manager come running! It takes a lot of hard work for a baby capybara to get enough attention at the office.

I could hear the Boss talking at the telephone. "Yes, we can do that . . . Oh, that soon? . . . We are working on another deadline, but tomorrow, we could have that to you tomorrow."

I followed The Boss to the Farm Manager's doorway and peeked past the tumbled-down makeshift barrier. The Farm Manager was focused over my fragrant potty bowl, swilling gently between her hands as she positioned it, transferring my projects to the portable bucket. The Boss held her breath but my attention-getting *"Eeep!"* was badly timed, and liquid sloshed wildly before waterfalling into the bucket, faster than usual. The bucket teetered but remained upright.

"The County wants those drawings tomorrow morning," said The Boss.

I took the opportunity to examine The Boss's office. The plants were all up, but there were no barriers at the bottom of the shelf. I pulled out a few loose papers and some skinny binders. I sniffed along the bookshelf until the wall forced me to turn. What's this, a wire? Where does it go? I turned again to follow it and stopped at a pair of shiny black shoes with gold buckles. Looking up I saw that The Boss was wearing those shoes.

"Out, now!" she said.

Fine, there were better projects waiting for me. I liked to "zing" the carpet. It was a nice dense industrial weave. If I picked up a bit between my big front teeth, The Boss would come running. That's because there was a kind of air space under there when I picked it up like a little circus tent, and it would make a resonant zoom-boing sound when I released it. That's not the only reason why The Boss would come running. She was quicker to arrive than the Farm Manager, but she didn't stick around to play. She liked to examine the tiny frayed fibers that appeared wherever my razor-sharp incisors bit the carpet.

"Stop that!" she said.

The Farm Manager and I took a lot of walks at work, out the door and down the carpeted hall to the bathroom. If she left me alone in the office I would *eep* and *eep* for her, so she took me with her. It was a good time to empty my potty bucket, so the Farm Manager, the bucket, and I would all mosey down there like a herd of turtles. The office next door was full of designer types and if I stopped at their doorway, *eep eep eep*ing, they all came running out to play with me.

"*Eeep!*" I said until they saw through the glass door that it was me who was *eep*ing. (That's all it takes me to get invited in. You should try *eep*ing sometime, it works great.) Farther down the hall, well beyond their door and awkwardly holding the fragrant bucket behind her back, the Farm Manager turned and apologized. A bunch of them had already rushed out to the hall to see me, then surged back into their office, talking to me and enticing me with a tantalizing array of shoelaces. Suddenly the star attraction, I could do no wrong. Cameras came out of hiding places and I struck a pose. I laid on the floor, I stood up, I sat on a chair, I was lifted onto a desk. When the Farm Manager returned, without the bucket this time, the questions began.

"It's from Australia, right?" they said.

I stopped going to work eventually, but the Farm Manager kept going for a long time after that without me. Now that I think about it, I never saw a single paycheck! Excuse me, but I need to ask the Farm Manager a question.

Chapter Two

My human brother reassures me that there are no alligators in my bathtub.

NO, I DON'T WANT TO GO BACK "TO THE WILD"

You might be surprised to learn how many rude people suggest that it is better to leave wild animals like me "in the wild." This is my first clue that they have no idea what they are talking about. I wasn't snatched from my South American capybara mommy by some scruffy poachers. My parents were carnies[7] from Texas. Their names were Bonnie and Clyde and they were featured as "giant rats." I'm not making this up. Without tails, the rat thing is kind of a stretch, but one hundred pound "rats" are still very impressive. When not on the road, all the

---

7   That's right, they worked in a traveling carnival sideshow.

carny animals lived on acres of grassy paradise. Anyway, that's where I was born, at the fancy farm, not on the road, though that would make a better story. "Born under the bright lights of the midway, within sight of the biggest Ferris wheel North of the Mississippi, eating discarded deep-fried Oreos and half-eaten corn dogs from day one!"

In the wild, capybaras are lucky to live six years[8]. Studies show that about 48% of wild capybaras survive to their second year. One very important capybara study in South America involved rounding up hundreds of capybaras and the researchers found only a few individuals in the 4 to 6-year-old range. Another study didn't find ANY that were older than four years old. The average age of wild capybaras is 1.2 years, about 14 months. That's not even old enough for us to get married! My parents were both about ten years old when they died, so they had it pretty good. My grandpa, Captain, lived to be seventeen!

So, these well-meaning folks who think I should be sent back to the wild, are they thinking I should join a carnival or something? Maybe they feel that at eight I have outlived my usefulness and should have been dead for the past two years? Or that the Farm Manager should have let me die when I was a baby? Maybe they think I should go back to live on the farm in Texas where Bonnie and Clyde came from. They died a few years ago, so it would be me, a pony, some goats, a hog, I don't know, but I would be the only capybara. Or maybe Arkansas; my parents were born in Arkansas. The first time I almost died, the Farm Manager phoned Mary Lee in Arkansas, remember that? That's where they were born. Mary Lee is retired now, but a while back she still had five senior capybaras about fifteen to seventeen years old. That seems like a pretty good place to live, but even though she's very proud of me, I can guarantee you she doesn't need a young whippersnapper like me riling things up around there.

That leaves going back to South America. All of the best capybara habitat, grasslands along the rivers, is already spoken for. Drop me off with a picnic lunch and I might last half a day before the natives spot me for an unwelcome

---

8   Lord, Rexford D.; *Capybaras: a natural history of the world's largest rodent*; Johns Hopkins University Press; 2009.

interloper. The resident capybaras would have me hightailing it into the rainforest where I'd get nabbed by the resident jaguar who would immediately recognize me for some witless City Slicker.

By most standards, that's exactly what I am: a city slicker. I have lived in the suburbs my entire life. My meals are delivered promptly, The Chambermaid straightens up daily, I subscribe to free grass delivery so I don't even have to graze if I don't want to. I have marked this territory so thoroughly that not one jaguar has ever been seen here. It's nearly perfect and I have no intention of leaving.

In comparison to those poor wild capys, my parents lived an exceptionally long, luxurious life. No thanks. I'm not going to move to some unsavory jungle. I think we have covered that question.

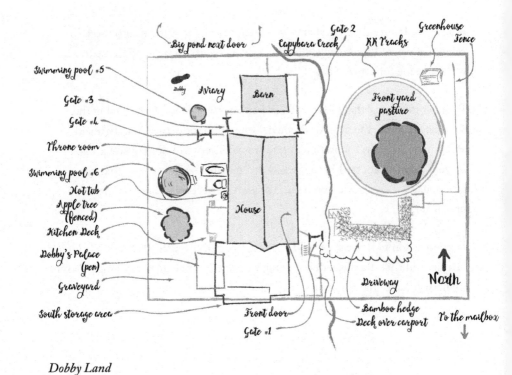

Dobby Land

FUN AND GAMES: TERRITORIAL MARKING

Capybaras have several methods of territorial marking: the morrillo, the anal glands, and plain old peeing and pooping around. It's kind of a big deal with rodents. Gerbils, for instance, have a gland on their belly, and they also leave little drops of urine around as they explore. Agoutis, a very busy South American rodent, bury their food and then pee on it so they can find it later. Such a sanitary habit. Guinea pigs have glands "back there" and rub butt grease on their territories. Very dignified. Rats, well, rats are revolting, and mark all over the place with everything they have at their disposal. Capybaras are multi-talented, too.

My favorite kind of marking is Category One: rubbing the top of my nose all over everything. It's a guy thing. Mature male capybaras have a scent gland on top of their enormous snout called a morrillo[9]. Mine was really really big and much greasier before my operation[10], but I am still diligent about marking everything with it. The Farm Manager says she can't smell it at all, but I know my marking technique is very effective because no other male capybaras have ever tried to claim my territory. Moseying through the garden, I tilt my head to mark gates, garden tools (while they are in use), plants, the cats, and I especially mark the Farm Manager. I like to mark the hem of her jackets and I do it over and over and over and over again. You can't be too thorough with morrillo marking.

If you have ever looked underneath a male capybara, you probably noticed a distinct lack of, well, male-ness. Our equipment is retractable, like an elephant or hippo, or dolphin. There is no need for vulgar display, we have other ways of demonstrating our manhood. For instance, we have fancy scent glands incorporated into that general butt-hole area. (I think I am supposed to call it an anus when I am talking to strangers, to be more polite.) Anyway, anal marking, Category Two, is simply one more of life's joys when you are a capybara. Not as good as marking with a morrillo, because that's only for boys, but it's a close second.

I like to rub my anal glands on the ground, like a dog, but my favorite kind of marking is to walk across something as I pee on it. It's mostly an outdoor activity, unless I am marking the kitchen. I like buckets a lot, but I have broken so many small buckets that way that there are only big ones left. Low branches

---

9   Big boy capybaras have a much bigger morrillo than the girls, so that's the best way to figure us out, if you care about gender. It only works on grown-up capybaras, though, so even experienced people make mistakes all the time.

10   I'll tell you about that later. I prefer not to dwell on such gruesome events. Let's move along now.

are really fun to walk over. They tickle. I walked over a hen one time. I walk over small shrubs, basketballs, and especially anything the Farm Manager leaves lying around. Like maybe her jacket, or her boots. Don't tell The Bartender but I have marked some of his gigantic shoes. Kidding! Maybe.

The Farm Manager seems most annoyed by Category Three marking: dribbling as I walk. It's fun and easy to do: just leave a trail of urine as you walk around. You don't have to walk over anything special like you do for Category Two marking. When I was about 5 months old, I started marking the bedroom carpet with urine. As I got older, there were more and more drops and it got darker, making it easier to see for The Bartender who cleaned it up with carpet cleaner during the day, and The Chambermaid who cleaned it up again with carpet cleaner every night after I went to bed. This color change is what happens as the anal glands mature and contribute their essence. It's the main reason why the living room and dining room became off limits to me. Of course, my dwindling territory reinforced my diligence in marking the only major territory left to me: the bedroom. I was also careful to mark the carpeted stairs up to the bedroom, starting with the landing. It's fun to leave a trail up the stairs, but at the landing I could walk lazy circles, dribbling continually until I achieve the desired effect. You might think this would be so satisfying it could not be surpassed, but I have a surprise for you! There is more marking!

Yes, indeed, I know you're all waiting to hear about Category Four, the trail of poop. The Farm Manager loves this game and she rushes to collect my deposits as soon as I make them, which I find very satisfying. This is especially true of the ones I deposit indoors, but outdoors she has even built me a special repository. Herbivores are not very efficient eaters, and like elephants, we process a lot of material. When I was quite young, the Farm Manager and The Bartender buried my contributions in the garden, but she quickly realized how undignified a hole in the ground is, and maybe it occurred to her how many holes there would eventually be. That's why she installed a commode in the back yard. She got a little crazy and put in a matching bathtub, lavatory, shower, and then hot water. I do like the ceremony at the throne, with the whooshing noise, and the clapping noise the seat makes as it drops. My own ceremony is lovely, as well.

My technique is worth noting. I carefully select a territory that requires marking and lay down an initial poop pile that can be quite large. Next I carefully turn 180 degrees so that my nose is directly above the first deposit. I take a big whiff and at the opposite end I lay down a very small deposit, the shape of a Hershey kiss. And *pouf*. When I am very pleased, my smile takes the form of piloerection[11]. That sounds kind of disgusting but it simply means that my hair stands on end. It is quite an attractive look, I'm told, like a porcupine. The result of this two-part deposit is that another animal visiting my territory can readily determine my size. And leave. I made that part up.

That's regular pooping, like when no one is looking. The other poop game I made up is a lot more fun, because it is a game for two. First I make a strategic deposit, not a very large one, but substantial enough to attract flies. Then I wait for the Farm Manager to scurry out to scrape it into a dustpan. She sprints to my throne room and I watch her lift the lid on my throne. She ceremoniously lowers my precious goods into the bowl and I listen for the whoosh and the clap of the lid coming down. Then I catch her attention and make another deposit! She scurries over to collect it as I stand aside and admire her technique. Sprint, whoosh and clap and what do you know? Yes, a third dainty deposit, the Hershey kiss! Sometimes I even do a little Doofus Dance[12] to celebrate, for this is a game that The Prince always wins. Unless she is really on top of her game and catches the deposit in her dustpan before it hits the deck.

---

11 Merriam-Webster definition of piloerection: "involuntary erection or bristling of hairs due to a sympathetic reflex usually triggered by cold, shock, or fright or due to a sympathomimetic agent." In other words, goosebumps. Try to work that gem into your next conversation.

12 Are you down here checking out this footnote because you want to know what a Doofus Dance is? Okay, it's easy. You know how a rabbit runs zig-zaggy, spins circles, skedaddles and zoomies all over the place like a maniac? Sometimes they simply leap up, spin a 180 in the air and land, cocking their head as if to ask if you noticed? That's called a "binky." Have you seen a guinea pig leap for joy, hopping around like it's legs are spring-loaded? That's called "popcorning." My special happy dance starts with a head wag. Next there is a butt wag (*not* twerking!), and then a wiggle and half-spin, a bit more head wagging, and finally I wiggle my ears. I guess I look like a doofus when I do it, so that's what the Farm Manager calls it.

HABITAT LOSS, THE BEGINNING OF THE END

In the beginning, when I weighed 5 pounds and was easy to pick up and carry around, I wandered around the house whenever someone was home. When I was home alone I had to live in a bathtub, but it didn't take me long to jump out and wander around the house whenever I wanted to. I was such a good boy, doing all my business in my potty bowl, and keeping my feet so clean. Still, it wasn't long before there were metal cages around all the electrical wires in the house. Soon after, gates started popping up here and there.

The Bartender's office was downstairs and even though it wasn't very interesting down there, he shut the door. There's still milk on a door at the bottom of the stairs, way down low at baby nose level. The Chambermaid will never clean it up so it's permanent proof that I used to own that territory, the landing at the bottom of the stairs. In fact, the stairs were my favorite playground. I kept a stash of stuffed toys at the top by my tiny donut shaped bed. No matter how many times I tossed those stupid toys down, they would magically migrate to the top again. A couple balls, some felt mice, a scruffy rabbit and a few IKEA rats, they all defied gravity and floated back up. The mice were fun to swing around by the tail before being jettisoned, but the rabbits made nice pillows for my tiny bed.

An interesting territory that was lost to me early was the little bedrooms down the hall. Something about wires and games. I don't really know much about what's there because a gate was installed there fairly early on. One time "somebody" left enough doors ajar for me to sneak all the way down the hall to check it out! My human sister was visiting and that's her old territory. She saw a shadow coming down the hall and naturally assumed it was the Farm Manager on all fours, creeping up to surprise her. Man, my human sister, she can really scream! The Farm Manager came to check, deftly dodging Dobby-deposits: minor samples, mind you. Well, she started hollering, too, and I got scared, spun around and high-tailed it out of there, without the tail, of course. Since then, it's been hard to find any doors open, but I keep checking.

For a long time, I was allowed into the living room, but dining rooms are always the best. There's nothing more fun than lurking under the table, nibbling this and that. I like to surprise guests by nipping their shoelaces into tiny worms though they are quick to notice a bite out of their shoe. I don't much like leather and when I started to lick the leather couch it was the end of couch surfing for me. Big swinging barrier half-doors were installed after I took the second bite out of the leather arm of the Farm Manager's vintage rosewood Eames chair. That is prime chewing, and I make a beeline for that chair whenever I get the chance. You might have seen photos of me standing outside the front door? I know the chair is in there and I still want to go in and bite it.

Even after I started sleeping outdoors, under the stars, I was allowed into the kitchen, the big upstairs bedroom, and, of course, the bathroom, up there where old Bathtub #2 and my first potty bowl lived. I had already been evicted from The Bartender's office downstairs, the little bedrooms down the hall, the living and dining rooms, but I was King of the Kitchen. Daytime I would hang out there, near the birds and guinea pigs that lived there. I nobly excused myself to trek up to the bathroom and mostly I came back down to hang with the motley herd in the kitchen. A couple of times I got caught sniffing around the closet and a new gate went up. That's when I started to mark the bedroom.

Sooner or later you will hear about how I eat my poop. When you are a capybara (or a rabbit or a guinea pig), it is always snack time. Mostly I eat my poop for breakfast in bed. The Chambermaid has learned to keep her mouth closed when she shakes out the blankets on my bed. On occasion, I leave pancakes in there. Coprophagy[13] can be kind of a messy business, though other capybaras seem to manage it with delicacy. I'm just a grubby guy. I'm also too lazy to leave my cozy bed when I need to pee, but it's my bed, I am The Prince, and I do as I like. My bed wasn't always outdoors, though, and that's why this chapter is called "Habitat Loss." When I was 5 months old I started to pee and poop in my indoor bedding and, coincidentally, right after that is when I started to sleep outdoors.

I never slept in the Farm Manager's bed because it is so high off the ground I

---

13 Merriam-Webster definition of coprophagy: the eating of feces that is normal behavior among many animals. I like this definition because it makes eating poop sound like a dignified activity.

couldn't get up there! Also, The Bartender takes up most of the space. So I slept on blankets on the floor right next to the head of the bed. It worked out well because there was a dust ruffle to chew up even though the wires were somehow caged so that I couldn't nip them. The bathroom with my potty bowl was only twenty baby steps away from my bedding. The bathroom also had a snack bar open all hours and a bowl of drinking water too small to stand in but too heavy to toss. This setup worked for quite a while.

The undoing started when I would walk all the way to the bathroom to drink water or eat a few potatoes, but then come back to my bedding to let loose with Niagara Falls. Mostly, I think the Farm Manager found it unnerving to be awakened by the fragrance of fresh urine only a few inches from her head. It happened a few times randomly, and then it became a morning ritual. The Chambermaid put a crib-sized waterproof pad between my bedding and the bedroom carpet. A couple weeks later, she put a large plastic sheet between my bedding and the bedroom carpet. Next she moved my bedding to the bathroom, on cold hard tile, and she put up a gate to make me stay there. Before you could say Jack Robinson, I was sleeping outside.

It was part of the larger plan, anyway. The only guidebook to pet capybaras available to the Farm Manager was *Capyboppy*, a book by Bill Peet. In it, the beginning of the end for poor Capyboppy was when it became a struggle to pen him up at bedtime[14]. He ended up at a zoo and it went rapidly downhill after that. The Farm Manager was determined to have a happy ending to this story. A neighbor gave us a used dog kennel and the Farm Manager set it next to the house at a decidedly rakish angle. The poor Bartender had to do some fancy carpentry to plug up the resulting gaps. Then the Farm Manager hauled a big bed in from the garden. (Don't all gardens have beds?) The Chambermaid put some blankets on it and we all slept out there together for a few nights. It was summer time and it was warm, and there were stars out, and it was glorious! I was so excited about my new outside bedroom that I didn't care when everybody stopped sleeping out there with me.

---

14 Open up your copy of *Capyboppy* and look at the picture on about page 40. It should be a picture of Capyboppy being carried out to the garage at bedtime. This is precisely what the Farm Manager wanted to avoid, and now I weigh 115 pounds. That's about 50 kgs. Way too heavy to carry.

The "underbed" is a pretty cool space, too!

Even though I had moved outdoors to sleep, I continued to traipse around the kitchen, stairs, and bedroom during the day. My potato bowl migrated to the kitchen, but my potty bowl stood ready in the shower. It was a nuisance for me to climb those stairs to reach the bathroom and I liked to mark the back yard. Days would pass, and The Chambermaid noticed that the potty bowl was still clean. It seemed silly to keep a clean unused potty bowl in there, one that had to be dumped and refilled twice daily so that she and The Bartender could use the shower. (She's so prissy that she won't stand in even a clean potty bowl while she showers!)

Of course, the best part about sleeping outdoors is that you are already outside when you wake up in the morning. Everything fun happens outside. There's grass to eat. There are wading pools and puddles. There are squirrels, crows, a pair of mallards, and dozens of little brown tweety birds. In the afternoon, we have a garden party with corn and other treats. There are ducks and hens and rabbits and two obnoxious geese who were babies with me.

That summer was amazing. I ate a couple of minor swimming pools and a pair of boots, learned how to tease the hens, and I barely noticed when a couple of gates went up in the house to keep me in the kitchen. Everything was perfect and then something terrible happened to the sun. It faded away and didn't make everything warm any more. It disappeared earlier each day, and the whole world started to shut down. Trees lost their leaves, some of the tweety birds disappeared, and it got very, very cold, especially at night. A heated kennel pad made my bed cozy and a wall-hung micathermic heater was installed to keep my bedroom from freezing.

One day it was so cold that I didn't want to go outside. I drank my bedtime milk in the kitchen and everybody seemed to forget about me. I wanted to go outside to my bed, but it was gol-danged cold out there! I paced at the door for a while and then set off to explore. A golden fence[15] had appeared in the bedroom and a moth-eaten collection of blankets covered the bedroom carpet, right up to the bed! Yep, the dust ruffle was still there, so I took a nip. The Farm Manager dashed over and fenced it off. I checked the bathroom. Yep, my trusty old potty bowl was still there. I stood on the bathroom tile and let 'er rip! The Chambermaid stared at me, stunned. To me, Lake Dobby on the bathroom floor seemed the appropriate non-verbal request to go outdoors. She threw a couple towels over the brand-new water feature, led me to the kitchen, and opened the outside door. Most days it was like the refrigerator but tonight it was like

---

15 I found out later that it was a brass colored exercise pen for little dogs, splayed out into a fence. Perfectly inedible, but I did eventually learn how to manipulate it to my advantage.

the freezer. I wanted the Farm Manager to fix it so I could sleep out there, but it stayed cold. She shut the door and I skulked back to the bedroom. Maybe I could sleep there. The Chambermaid was quite surprised when she checked on me later. She probably thought I was asleep on the nice bed she had made up for me, but I had been in stealth mode. First, I had laid down a poop trail of tears, and second, I had walked through it. Third, I had walked through it again, and fourth . . . yep. I was quite pleased with my statement. The world had changed without my permission and I was miffed. It had been five months since I had slept indoors and I thought for sure I ought to be sleeping outdoors today, too! She led me to the kitchen door one more time, and then she opened it. Dagnabbit, that's cold! No way I was going to sleep out in that so-called weather.

It was a long and busy night. I would poop and distribute. The Chambermaid would take up the blankets and put down new ones. She was a magician that night because the blankets kept on a-coming. She was very excited about this game, and as the pile of poopy blankets rose to the rafters, I wondered why she wasn't washing them, but then she hadn't been washing anything for a while.

The next day and the next night were the same. I kept hearing the same words over and over again: *minefield, brokenwasher, freezing,* and *@#$%^&**. Then it started raining and we were back to normal. Except that nothing was ever normal again. The Farm Manager and I eventually wrote a Scientific Paper[16] about this nasty little episode. I stuck it in the back of this book so that you can read it.

---

16 Effect of Climate Change on *Hydrochoerus hydrochaeris* by Stacy Thomas Winnick and Prince Dobby Winnick. It's back there in the Appendix.

HABITAT LOSS, THE FINAL STRAW

The shower stall potty bowl disappeared around the same time that the Golden Fence appeared in the bedroom. Zig-zagging across the room, it looked flimsy but no amount of smacking into it yielded a usable breach. First it chopped the room in half, cutting me off from the most important marking and nibbling territory: The Bartender's shoes. I know this isn't possible because the house is not haunted, but that Golden Fence inched its way across the bedroom, shrinking my marking grounds a wee bit each and every day. It crept closer to the door, even as it blocked access to the closet and my old sleeping spot by the bed! Finally, the Golden Fence was so close that I couldn't get into the bedroom at all. I was left with access to the potty bowl in the shower stall, period. What was the point of wandering up there at all, then? My entire bedroom territory was now reduced to a narrow corridor into the bathroom.

I still had the stairs, the hall, and the kitchen. Then one day substantial gates magically appeared at the doorways to the living room. The Golden Fence moved downstairs, first cutting off the stairs, then the hall, eventually corralling me into a miniscule space adjacent to the kitchen door. That shrunk my kitchen territory by more than half. I was outside all the time anyway, and nothing changed for a long time. If the door wasn't quite closed, I could go in and out of the kitchen myself by grabbing the edge of the door with my front teeth and pulling. Sometimes I was hasty and grabbed the trim and ripped off a hunk. Oops! The kitchen door has lots of little panes of glass framed by wood. It's great because I can see through the door. And I can grab the frame between the panes with my teeth and open the door that way, too. Oops, there went a ripped chunk of door! Pretty soon there was metal edging on the door frame and Plexiglas covering the lower half of the door.

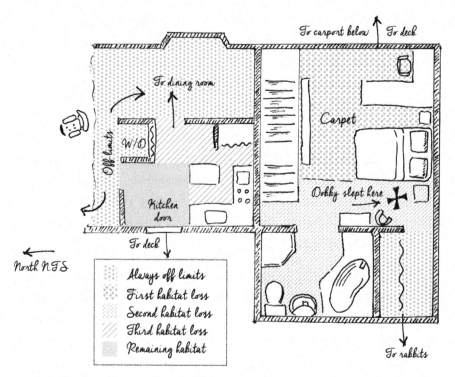

I might as well declare myself an Endangered Species.

One of the Prince Dobby Approved improvements was my very own doorknob. The Bartender installed a tiny mushroom-shaped wooden knob at snout level on the outside of the door. Then he put up an automatic door closer and jammed a chunk of wine cork into the strike plate so the door wouldn't latch closed. Now I could easily come and go to the back yard whenever the mood struck me.

This new freedom kind of went to my head, because the very next day, I showed the Farm Manager that I had learned to go in and out like a champ. I also showed the Farm Manager that I could open the other door, too. This was not quite a door, though. It was the Golden Fence. I had been watching the Farm Manager go in and out of the Golden Gate, and now I showed her that I could do that, too! I picked up the fence with my teeth and ever so gently swung it open and stepped into the now verboten kitchen area. She was very excited about this!

She was so excited, in fact, that within a day or two, a carpenter showed up with two humungous walls, a real doorknob, and some linoleum. I was swooshed away to the back yard and when I was allowed back into the kitchen, the deal was sealed: my kitchen area was permanently downsized. Never again would I set foot in any other part of the house, unless somebody accidentally left a door open.

Like an elephant, capybaras never forget. If the door is open, even just an itty bitty crack, I've got my nose in there, pushing through. Like a hawk, I watch that door constantly. If it's ajar, I am through it. I am a donkey when I am ready to go back inside the house from the front yard. Instead of walking around the house, through the storage area and the back yard, and up the steps to the kitchen door—you know, the way we went out—I stand by the front door. I have never gone through that door, but I know that The Chair is there, and that the kitchen is only a few small steps beyond it. Mark my words, someday I will mark my living room again. When I do, I'll post it as my status on Facebook so everyone can celebrate.

THE SECOND TIME I ALMOST DIED

I don't like to admit this, but I am a real wuss. I'm very tough in the back yard. I patrol the boundaries and double check where breaches have been known to occur. I'd say it's secure 99% of the time. The aviary is secure, too. Nothing can even drop in from above because there is a wire roof. I don't need to patrol it because my two sergeants, tomcats named Kitty Hawk and Grover Cleveland, cover that territory for me. They constantly look for openings because they want to get out. (They don't seem to realize they are actually in *jail!*) If there is a way out, they'll be out yesterday.

So anyway, the second time I nearly died I was in the very vulnerable front yard. I was minding my own business, grazing, you know, and the Farm Manager was kind of over there, somewhere. The bamboo hedge is grown up so I couldn't see the car that parked in the driveway. Nothing happened for a while, and then I heard the car door open and shut. A minute later someone lurched through the gate. Two someones: a human that I knew with a smaller yellow thing dancing around at the end of a leash. A dog, a very small dog. The human hadn't seen me and the dog was too excited at first to notice me. *"Bark!"*

"What the heck?" Now that was something I hadn't anticipated. The dogs I see at the veterinary clinic never bark. I like them and I get very pouffy when they recognize me as royalty. So I wasn't expecting to hear such a belittling statement from this little dog. And that's when I did something silly: I bolted! Instead of running away, though, I ran right toward them. My escape route was on the other side of them, but I had one very sharp turn to make on my way to safety and that's when my ersatz Vibram© FourFinger soles failed me. I skidded into the turn and crashed into an old terra cotta planter. (It was replaced by a safer plastic model soon after my near death incident.)

Criminy that hurt! The entire side of my face was bloody! I was certain that my lip had been torn off, because I was bleeding all over the place and nobody could see what was underneath the goo. You know how face wounds are, they bleed rivers of blood. The Farm Manager tried to wash off the bloody mess with water and get close enough to look but I kept moving. Were my big bucky beavers (my incisors) broken? She gave me an apple, hoping I would stay still while I ate and allow her to examine me. Ha ha ha, she's so funny! Now I had apple froth mixed with the water and coagulated blood and I was starting to look like a zombie. My teeth seemed okay, but my upper lip probably had a gash, a hole, a tear, or a combination. Well, lip is not quite the correct word, it was that zone between my lip and my nostril, that big soft place under my nose. The place where you would stick on one of those fake mustaches. Or give me a kiss if I didn't look quite so much like the star of a horror flick.

As if that wasn't traumatic enough, the Farm Manager connected the leash to my harness and we headed out Gate #2 and down the front garden stairs toward the car. Once I am beyond Gate #1, the last place I am interested in is the car. There is a tiny creek and waterfall, big ferns and lots of Not For Dobby plants to eat. I can see the car, parked in the driveway, back door open, the ramp in place.

The leash is tyrannical, and yet with the proper technique, I can slip out of the harness in a heartbeat because capybara shoulders are the shape of a football. The leash functions perfectly if the human is situated behind the capybara. That puts tension on the leash and in turn keeps the harness snug on my shoulders. If I simply turn to face the human, suddenly the leash is in tension the opposite way, pulling the harness off my shoulders and over my head. And I'm free! (This didn't happen; I needed to add some drama to the story.[17]) I did wander here and there, turning around, eating plants, turning around again, bucking a little. I like to check out the cars and carport, too. The Mystery Gate to the south storage area is there, too. I know it goes to the back yard, but for some reason I'm not allowed to come to the front yard that way. It's intriguing, though, and I always like to check it out.

Lots of people like to come when I go for a car ride. You are probably thinking it is only me and the Farm Manager, with her driving, and me riding shotgun. It's fun to think about me sticking my head out like a dog, changing the radio station, sipping my Big Gulp. But, no. Capybaras have to sit in the back. And that's why there is always a bunch of people in the car. By bunch I mean The Bartender. He drives, and the Farm Manager spends the whole first five minutes keeping me from climbing into the front seat to nibble on his ears. Lately, there is a fence between the front seat and the back. The Farm Manager sits right next to me and I nibble on her ears instead. The split back seat is flopped down except for where she sits. There are blankets everywhere, three or four deep in some places. My special pirate bed is back there, usually a white rabbit rug, maybe some corn and lettuce in a big bucket.

Eventually, I agreed to approach the ramp into the car. That involved as many raisin bribes as I thought I could get away with and then some dramatic slipping and sliding before I scrambled on up. The Farm Manager climbed into the back with me and I started to shake and sweat, turning around and around, not settling down for the ride. I get kind of car sick, but I still managed to get my blood-and-froth zombie face all over everything without revealing the status

---

17 This is so important that you might want to turn down a corner on this page or use a highlighter. You may need to review the harness technique in a few more pages. That's a hint.

of my lip. The Bartender drove for days on end and we finally pulled into the cramped parking lot in front of the veterinary clinic. He got out of the driver's seat, slamming his door, and walked around, opened my door, and put the ramp up to the door.

Unfortunately, the veterinary clinic was next door to a pet food store. Someone had left their dog in the car while they were shopping and it was barking. *"Bark!"* I recoiled in horror. No way I was going to get out of the car. Ever. The Farm Manager went in and out of the clinic a couple times and eventually the entire staff came out to the car: two veterinarians, a couple assistants, and some curious sous-staff. They all stood around talking, and Dr. F leaned in, attempting to get a good look at my face. Not on your life, sucker! They talked about sedating me, but I wasn't bleeding to death any more by then. Nobody volunteered to stick their fingers in my mouth and poke around the cheek to see if there were any holes or broken parts. They could see that my incisors were fine. Even smacking into that pot hard enough to rip my face off wasn't enough to break my big chompers. The decision was finally made to allow my mystery injury to heal and if necessary, consult regarding reconstructive surgery at a later date.

I didn't die that time, either, of course. It had been a very bad cut, but there were no holes, no loose skin flaps, no missing body parts. There was a pretty good gash but it didn't interfere with eating corn, thank goodness. I did end up with one heck of a scar, though it isn't as dramatic as some facial scars I have seen on wild capybaras on the internet. Those big boys out in the Amazon basin must run into a lot of alligators. You've got to watch out when you're swimming!

Chapter Three

Not For Dobby!

MY ADORABLE FEET

I have fourteen toes. Thank goodness capybaras weren't responsible for the numbering system because base 14 would be really awkward. You're probably wondering how on earth I can have fourteen, but if you have seen a guinea pig, you know the answer. My great big back feet have three toes and magnificent webbing, like a beaver. They're great for swimming, but they're also pretty good for walking on mud or the sandy bottom of a streambed. Because of the webbing, they keep me from sinking into mud or other squishy things I step in.

My front feet have more interstitial spaces for holding onto that kind of junk, but that's about all they're good for. They are much smaller, but not T-Rex small; that would be embarrassing. They are exactly like big guinea pig feet: they have four toes and they are pretty useless. What I mean is that I can't hold my corn with them the way a mouse or a squirrel or a porcupine can. If they were true paws, it would be very classy, but they are legs with toes at the bottom. I'm not complaining. I can eat corn-on-the-cob without hands and that is much more impressive than The Chambermaid's ability to fold a fitted bed sheet. I'm suggesting that our next evolutionary goal might be functional paws. Maybe I need to do a Kickstarter for that.

Four toes, though, in the front, and times two feet is eight toes total in the front, three on each back foot, so six back there, and *voila!* Fourteen digits!

The webbed back feet are pretty cool, but they do have some other interesting attributes. Baby capy fur is soft, as it should be. But mature capybara fur is thick and not uniformly round but almost longitudinally faceted. It even has nap, so that you can rub it one way but it's kind of barbed going the other way. In some flash photos, the unevenness of the individual hairs reflects light and if you "enhance" the photo it looks all sparkly. Not in a good way though, it makes the photo look like there's "snow" like when the TV cable is acting up, but only on me of course, and the rest of the photo is normal. I'm not quite that magical!

We were talking about feet, though. The fur on my feet is totally soft and babyish, as if two different designers did the fur and then couldn't compromise so we got both. My foot fur is short and soft and distributed much more densely than my body fur, which is quite shockingly sparse. It is also a very attractive gray, like moleskin, while my coarse body fur ranges from blonde to red to brown. My foot fur lies snug to my foot, while my body fur has trouble making up its mind what it wants to do. When I'm happy, it sticks straight out and that's when the shocking part happens because you can easily see right down to my skin.

And my skin is leather, which is another point. My foot skin is, well, skin, not leather. This is another poor evolutionary choice, to have delicate skin on your foot. Having leather everywhere else was a good decision, to have Jaguar-proof skin. The feet, though, should have sturdy covering, too, don't you think? I get little bumps and cuts on my feet all the time, not because I'm clumsy, but for some other reason that I can't think of. The foot boo-boos heal in a day, though. That's a good way to handle it. I don't think anything else in the world heals as fast as a capybara foot boo-boo.

The other wonderful part about my fourteen toes is my fourteen toenails! Baby capybara toenails are sharp as razors, but after we grow up the edges dull and the toenails grow and some smarty-pants always suggests that the toenails ought to be trimmed. Think about the logistics of that for a minute. You can't exactly take your capybara to a nail salon, plunk down a diet Coke next to him, and ask him to put his paws up on the table. For most procedures with capybaras, we have to be sedated. Second, my toenails were too hard to cut and started to bleed as soon as the Dremel[18] touched them! So we never entertain that notion any more.

My toenail material is interesting stuff. It isn't at all like human toenails. It seems like they would be like goat hooves, but they aren't that hard. They are like emu toes, hockey pucks, Vibram© shoe soles, vulcanized rubber. I scamper around on concrete a lot so mine have never gotten very long. Wild capybaras walk around in soft squishy mud all day long, and the Amazon basin has a dearth of nail salons, so I'm thinking super-long toenails are not going to be a pressing issue.

---

18 A Dremel is a swanky rotary tool that veterinarians use to grind off our toenails. It's more fun than cutting nails with clippers because it plugs in and makes noise.

The biggest foot problem we have is frostbite. Obviously, this is not a problem in some locations, but I live where it snows. The Farm Manager gets panicky when the ground freezes. She begs me to come indoors (Why doesn't she bribe me with corn or banana chips?) and tells me horror stories of some capybaras in Canada and New York who got frostbite. Apparently, not all foot boo-boos heal quickly. The problems start when the feet get infected, and the end of the story is too sad to be included in this book. I don't really like walking around on frozen ground, anyway, so I usually just tiptoe back into the kitchen and make a statement[19].

LET'S TAKE A WALK

Visitors wonder if being a capybara is like being a dog. No, it's not, and it's not like being a cat, either. Those guys are both predators: hunting, carnivorous animals. I am an herbivorous rodent. If you want to be persnickety about it, I am a graminivore,[20] a grazing animal like a donkey. Or a goose. I live in a herd, I graze most of the day, and I am a prey animal. Bottom of the food chain. I am the animal dogs and cats hunt to eat. Predators have eyes in front of their head, because they need depth perception more than they need to see what's behind them. My eyes are strategically located on the side of my head so that I have a 360-degree view. You can't sneak up on me! Plus, like guinea pigs, I can sleep with my eyes open, so nobody can sneak up on me from the front or back, day or night. How does all this make me a different kind of pet, then?

---

19 When we get to the part about clicking, there's a link to a video of me getting angry at snow.
20 A graminivore is a plant eating animal that mostly eats grass. In fact, capybaras eat bromeliads and all kinds of water plants, too. And corn on the cob, don't forget that!

Rodents live in fear. Even hamsters are fierce sometimes. Have you ever made the mistake of reaching into a hamster cage during the day? You got bit! That's right, they're nocturnal so that tiny devil is asleep and you are the monster that tapped him on the shoulder while he was dreaming about sunflower seeds. How about cute, cuddly guinea pigs? They are cute and cuddly if you can catch them! Most expert guinea pig wranglers have a technique for nabbing them that involves outsmarting them. It isn't as easy as it sounds. Capybaras are more like donkeys. You're not going to catch one, but you may be able to convince it to cooperate, to an extent.

Why would a rodent want to go for a walk in the first place? Some pet capybaras do go for walks, but they are exceptional. Most of us prefer to stay home, in our own territory where we know every inch of ground. At home we know which places are always safe, and where we are more vulnerable. We know where the best grass is, we know where there is deep water to hide in, we know where the chicken food is if we get hungry.

Most importantly, we know where border breaches are most likely. There are three ways into the back yard: through the kitchen door, through the aviary, and the scariest place of all, through the south storage area. The kitchen door has bells on it, and it is the most likely place for an intruder to enter my territory. It's mostly the Farm Manager or The Bartender, but I often entertain visitors, and they always come through the kitchen. The aviary has a reliable early warning system: Norman the goose! There are three gates that open and close with a clunk before you get into the back yard, and there is a fourth gate to enter before you even get to the first gate! Hmm that makes it the second gate. So four gates on that side, and I can hear them all open and shut before the boogey man gets into my yard. The south storage area has only two gates and The Bartender likes to come around that way because he likes to haul stuff around. He usually lets me know he is coming, but not always. Then I bark at him.

"Hey Dobby!" That's how my favorite neighbor, Connor, scared the heck out of me one time. He poked his head over the fence and now we know what I do when I am scared out of my skin: I race for my pool, scramble up the stairs and dive in! I have some other safe areas in the back yard. I can hide behind the pool, I can hunker down in mud, I can hide under the stairs or in my bed. I'm glad I picked brown fur because it blends in with all kinds of things: fences, piles of leaves—I can even hide in a flock of ducks! I have so many options that sometimes the Farm Manager has a hard time finding me!

So let's take that hypothetical walk. It is going to start out exactly the same way as going to the front yard to graze. Well, maybe. I am used to going out there in the afternoon, so if you want me to take that walk in the morning, I'm probably going to balk. The only reason we go to the front yard at odd times is when I have to go to my island cabin, or to the vet, *in the car*. No thank you. I lied: Sometimes I *beg* to go to the front yard at odd times. I love noisy machinery, so if there is lawn mowing or chain-sawing (my personal favorite) I need to investigate. I also love to graze at dusk. Sometimes I stay out there late, but other times I beg to go back out there for seconds. That's kind of a summertime thing. Sometimes I am ravenous and there's usually corn out there. But going out there at odd times is my prerogative.

So, the best bet for a walk is the afternoon. If everything looks normal—the Farm Manager dressed in her muddy boots and barn coat, she's got the corn (*very* important!) and the harness (groan)—then we're set. The leash has to clip onto the harness *before* Gate #2 opens to the front yard. The minute that happens, the wheels in my head begin to whir and spin, and an enormous question mark starts to form above my head. What the heck? I gotta figure we're going to the vet. *No, thank you.* Now you can flip back a few pages and re-read that part about the harness/leash technique. Or you can imagine me spinning and bucking down the path, the Farm Manager trying her darnedest to stay *behind* me, all the while pushing me ahead, to where she wants to go.

For the sake of argument, let's say that I am willing to go for a walk this time. My harness and leash are magically already on. Gate #2 swings wide, I saunter down the path, wait patiently for Gate #1 to open, ease my way down the stairs, and I'm at the driveway. Who gets to decide where we go on this walk? The puny little Farm Manager, or the big handsome capybara? I'm picking *me*. Do you know where I want to go? The back yard, but through the south storage area! It's like the Northwest Passage. I know that it goes through, but I've never been allowed to investigate from this side. I did escape the front yard once, and even though I could have run away, or at least to the driveway, all I did was check out the cars in the carport. (Why don't I get to ride in the convertible? The Farm Manager has this sweet ride, but no capybaras allowed! She says it's because there is no back seat. Harumph!)

I actually did take a walk once. It was a herd migration: the Farm Manager, The Bartender, and me. "Somebody" decided to go to the mailbox. At our house, the mailbox is down the street and around the corner. We followed the regular routine: going out to the front yard through the aviary, stopping at the storage area to put on my harness. The leash went on, we dragged each other down the path to Gate #1, stumbled down the stairs to the driveway, and the car door was not open. There was no ramp in evidence. I did not know this was possible. The leash is on and I'm going where, exactly? I took matters into my own hands and headed into the carport to check out The Bartender's big red car. *Boring*. The Farm Manager's convertible roadster is much more interesting. In the corner beyond the ragtop were some actual rags, boots, caps, gloves and bottles of things to taste test.

"Get him away from there!" The Bartender started scurrying around as the Farm Manager tried to coax me away from the snack items. Okay, fine, let's check the south storage area. I squeezed past the cars and the Farm Manager was forced to squeeze through the same narrow passage. I discovered some delicious potted plants near the stairs up to the south storage gate but was distracted by a fistful of dandelion greens The Bartender held out to me. We moved down the driveway and I began nosing around in the shrubbery along the side.

"Help me get him away from the rhododendrons. *Not For Dobby!*" Yes, there are a bunch of those out there. In the front yard, they are all fenced off. I'm not very interested in them, they smell pretty nasty, but any "Not For Dobby's" are intriguing. There are a few right by the front stairs. There are lots of them across the street, and all the neighbors here have them. I should check those out. I head across the street, the Farm Manager directly behind me, because, the leash. The Farm Manager immediately disagreed with my travel plans.

"Oh no," she said. "Their yard isn't fenced and if he sees that stream and follows it down, I'm not sure we can follow him! Plus, the stream flows from that huge wetland next door. See where it streams under the gap in the fence? Is that hole big enough for him to sneak through? It isn't big enough for me unless I get down on my belly and crawl through! If he goes upstream through there, we'll have to drive around with the car, find him over there, coax him into the car, and drive him home. We'll never be able to walk him home from way over there, that is, if he decides he wants to leave the wetland at all."

The Farm Manager is getting pretty excited about the stream! It's much bigger than the little creek at our house, and now I'm getting pretty excited about it, too! The Bartender was suddenly getting excited about it, too! Wait, no, he was excited about something else. The Bartender waved another handful of dandelion greens at me.

"Dobby! Look at this! For *Dobby!*" He was waving the greens frantically, now, and was slowly backing his way down the street. I love dandelion greens, but I'm too lazy to pick through the grass for them. They are tastiest when you munch a bunch. The Farm Manager picks them for the guinea pigs, puts them in these little buckets. I stick my schnozzola in there while she is picking and eat them all in one bite. A handful is very enticing, so I turned around and followed The Bartender back up the neighbor's driveway and into the street.

He kept walking backwards with those greens and wouldn't let me eat them! So I stopped. Hmmm. I could smell the front yard and see our driveway. I started walking toward the driveway and my yard.

"Wait, Dobby! Dick, bring those greens over here and give them to him. Go try standing in our driveway. He usually doesn't walk toward you. Here, Dobbs, you can have these dandelions now."

So now my mouth is foaming and dandelion juice green, the Farm Manager and I are standing in the street, and The Bartender is blocking my path toward home. When capybaras walk in a herd, we kind of bump into each other when we walk. That's why the Farm Manager gently nudged my brake light area with her knee. I walked forward a couple steps and turned to look at her. Again with the knee, so I walked a couple more steps and sat down. This was making no sense. The car was over there, the front yard was over there, and we were not going there. Someone was mixed up.

"C'mon, Dobby, let's go for a walk!" The Farm Manager must have said this a hundred times in the next few minutes. The Bartender approached, I moved away from him, the Farm Manager nudged my tailgate with her knee, I walked a couple steps and sat down. Repeat. Soon we were in front of the house next door, and the scent of my front yard was becoming fainter with every step. We were almost 1/3 of the way to the mailbox and I was slowing down. Or was I? At the next nudge, I veered wildly and took almost twenty steps. As I approached the garden of the next house, the Farm Manager tugged at my leash, calling over her shoulder to The Bartender.

"He's headed for the azaleas! They are as toxic as the rhododendrons. Get behind him on this side and try to get him back to the other side of the street!"

Vrooom-shush. I stopped moving. What was that thing? A Metro bus passed between me and the far away mailboxes, stopped at the corner, ejected a human who briskly walked away from us. What the hay?

"Maybe we shouldn't cross the street, stay on this side. We don't have to go all the way to the mailboxes. I forgot about the bus." The Farm Manager seemed to be backtracking on her "Take a Walk" challenge. The Bartender was looking skeptical at this point, too. Then the dog walker appeared. On the street where we had seen the bus, an athletically attired human had two dogs by two leashes. They had been moving the opposite direction that the bus had traveled, but they were inexplicably swerving our direction, now. I smelled the dogs and the dogs smelled me. They had stopped walking and were staring at me. The human at the end of the leashes was analyzing the situation and the question mark dangling over her head was enormous. The dogs were vacillating between High Alert, Attack, and Run for Your Life! I may look like a big fool but I knew what to do: I ran home.

The Farm Manager may look like a little fool, but she immediately calculated my top speed and compared it to her own. She also recognized that I would run home, dropped the leash, and hoped for the best. Like a Porsche 911 RSR, I raced for home, hugging the ground with my competition racing feet, taking the curves close to the limit. I splashed through the ever-present driveway puddles and scrambled up the rickety stairs, leash flapping behind me, miraculously unsnagged on the myriad hooks and snares lining the path[21]. Gate #1 was still open and I continued past the front door stairs, past the now shut back yard Gate #2, and all the way around the corner, past the train shed (don't ask) to my Safe Corner, the farthest possible front yard location from the mailboxes.

I was placidly contemplating the pond and wetland next door when the Farm Manager and The Bartender reached me, gasping and panting, faces red, hats missing, twigs and branches stuck in their hair. The Farm Manager stooped down next to me and removed the leash.

"I think somebody needs a piece of corn," she said.

---

21 During another escapade, my harness caught on a picket. I was galloping so fast that the plastic buckle shattered, leaving the empty harness dangling on the fence. It's the only time I have been naked in the front yard!

RANDOM ABANDONMENT

That's a somewhat sensational chapter heading. In fact, there is always a human here, but it isn't always the Farm Manager. Sometimes it's The Bartender. It has even been my human sister or human brother. The Farm Manager does abandon me, though. After all this time, it has become clear that she eventually returns, but it isn't an ideal situation. I think she should move out to the back yard with me permanently, and I'm sure she will someday, but so far, I am ready to settle for having her somewhere around the premises at all times.

In fact, right from the start, the Farm Manager left me behind. We would get up in the morning, have some milk and everything would be going just fine. Then she would suddenly race out the door. She would stay away for all the best parts of the day, wait for the sunny parts to end, then come skulking back after dark. The Bartender was home with me all day, but to tell you the honest truth, sometimes even he would leave, for hours at a time. Plus, he isn't nearly as attentive as the Farm Manager. Kind of a glorified baby-sitter, he meets all my needs, but we're talking capybara royalty here. I deserve to be spoiled rotten, 24/7.

From time to time, the situation rapidly deteriorates. I think the Farm Manager and The Bartender go to the moon or something. Those are the times when I find myself face-to-face with an actual pet-sitter. He is a stellar pet-sitter, don't get me wrong. He's a prince, like me! Still, I can't imagine being friends with him, because it is too stressful with The Farm Manager gone. He likes me and I respect him for being so persistent and prompt. In some ways, he is much more efficient than the Farm Manager. I can't believe anybody would want to deal with our nasty hissing cats and even those ducks and hens (especially Princess Blur) can be obnoxious. I think he even feeds the guinea pigs! He's here without warning. Suddenly there's no grazing in the front yard, no afternoon Garden Party with my hens, and believe it or not, I'm not even allowed in the kitchen! It's pretty bleak, but it's always during summer when I live outside anyway, and the detention never lasts very long.

A couple of times I have discovered that the Farm Manager and The Bartender have both left the planet and either my human brother or human sister is the baby-sitter. You might think this is not such a bad deal, but I am suspicious of them. When the regular pet-sitter is here, he's nearly a stranger, and being wary, I am well behaved around him. He's very professional and when he's here it's obvious that something serious is happening. When my human brother or human sister stay here, it's a little loosey-goosey. I'm suspicious that they have done something to the Farm Manager and The Bartender. Are they locked in the basement? Maybe they're sitting in the car in the driveway. You see, we are family, and everybody should be here at the same time. My human brother and human sister break the rules all the time, though. They stay here for a couple days, then they leave for months. Or they stay for months and then go away for a couple years, and then come back. It's very unnatural. That would never happen in a herd. Once you leave the herd, you pretty much don't come back. This crazy herd breaks all of the rules, all of the time, in every way you can imagine. I don't understand it, but I have come to accept it.

A TRIP TO THE CABIN

Every once in a while, they take me with them. This is one of those theoretical "good times" that never works out quite as well as you think it might.

The Farm Manager has a teeny tiny cabin on a big island out in the ocean. It's a car ride and a ferry ride in the car, and then another car ride to get there. The first time the herd went out there for the weekend, I was a baby. A hop up into the back of the car and I was ready to go! By the time the Farm Manager had loaded my blankets and white rabbit rug, my bed, lettuce, corn and potatoes, milk and milk bowl, hay and bucket, two Golden Fences, a barrier grid between the front and back seats, potty bowl and lots of shabby towels, I was already busy chewing up the seat belts. By the time she finished loading her personal equipment, people-food and the handicapped sparrow who lived with us, I was taking bites out of the car door. Then The Bartender got in the special driver's seat with the wheel toy, we waited and waited for my human sister to get in (I'm jealous that she gets to ride shotgun!), and off to the cabin we crawled, like a herd of turtles.

Washington State is known for its fabulous ferry system and the ridiculously long ferry waiting lines that snake along the edge of the roads leading to the official ferry parking lots. The ferry itself is like an enormous whale who eats your whole car and then farts it out again a while later. During the ride over, The Farm Manager indulged in her favorite ferry lunch of clam chowder and popcorn. The Bartender and my human sister both disappeared while I ate a head of lettuce and spewed frothy green juice onto my car blankets. The next car ride was short but they aren't ever much fun after the first five minutes, and I was ready to explore when we got to the cabin.

The car door swung open and I was stunned by the sudden change from hot sweaty capybara atmosphere to crispy wet forest air. The yard smelled like a deer convention, and there seemed to be a serious rabbit problem somewhere under the laundry room. It was like landing on Mars and I was confused by the alien stinkiness of everything. Prey animals are wary in new territories and this one didn't even have security fences! I huddled close to the Farm Manager as she kicked my butt up the little staircase to the safety deck. Little capybaras are perfectly obedient and well behaved, though, and can stay indoors. I lurched through the open door and was shocked again.

The cabin air was dry and dusty with a hint of bugs in the corners and spiders in the bathtub. While the sparrow got himself settled, blinds were raised, curtains and windows opened wide, and the refrigerator door opened and closed a dozen times. Nobody watched the capybara version of Sherlock Holmes examine the lower 25% of the cabin. Under-bed dens with delicious bed skirts, edible fringed rugs, towels dangling at a tantalizing morrillo-marking distance from the floor, chair and table legs to gnaw, and best of all, unprotected electrical cords! Suddenly I was thrust back out the door to the safety deck! Unfolded Golden Fences now straddled both ends of the deck and an empty potty bowl had been unceremoniously dropped between them. Harrumph!

The Farm Manager brought out water for the potty bowl, milk (hurray!), potatoes, apples, and a fistful of hay. She plopped herself down—a bit too hard—into a dusty plastic chair. A weary sigh bordering on a wail escaped her as she closed her eyes and lifted her pale face to the sun. Me too. Pacific Northwest sun is precious, indeed.

After approving the local grass, the five water-potato/apple-milk-hay-and-grain offering bowls, and tossing the pathetic toy, a toilet paper tube, I was ready to join the herd indoors. The electrical cords had mysteriously disappeared, but I had missed nibbling some baskets during my earlier foray. Incredibly, there were now dozens of tantalizing puzzle pieces to examine. The best surprise of all was that I had my own couch! It was like the other couches except for the color, and from my new perch, I could see everything and everybody! I liked the cabin and was finally getting used to the smells when suddenly everything happened in reverse and we all went back home.

Many milk-times passed and I forgot about the cabin. A few times the Farm Manager disappeared for a day and showed up late with a bucket of grass from the cabin. I could smell the salt air and the deer and the rabbit poopies on it. The dirt clinging to the roots was peculiarly sandy. Her shoes had picked up the sand and salt air fragrance, too. And then one day, instead of going to graze in the front yard, she snapped the leash onto my harness and we sauntered out to the car. (Not really, but you know the drill now, right?)

When the ears are chewed off, it is still a rabbit?

This trip, we discovered that my big backside took up much more of the back seat space than it had before. There wasn't room for even a sparrow back there. Now there was a dog crate in the back of the car, but it turned out that's where all the Farm Manager's stuff rode so I couldn't chew up her clothes or shoes. I realized we weren't going to the vet. There was too much equipment involved. The car bounced and jiggled and moved from side to side and then I started to sweat and drool and pace and I might have even pooped on my blanket. The car stopped and salty air swooshed in through the suddenly half-open windows. I started to relax but the car started again, drove slowly for a couple minutes and stopped. The salt air was heavy and damp. And then the car began to move slowly up and down, back and forth, but not in a predictable way. Was it doing lazy figure eights? Was it trying to swim or fly? My stomach protested, but the Farm Manager and The Bartender refused to listen. I vaguely remembered some wooziness like this in my past, but my big boy stomach was fighting with my equilibrium and a large percentage of my gut was in revolt. The car engine started again and I wondered about all that moving around, and how did that happen with the car turned off? As The Bartender drove us away I saw that we were coming out of the mouth of that great huge boat! Did it really eat us and now we were getting thrown up? Or was I mistaken about which end we came out of? Did the boat just poop us out? My thoughts were abruptly curtailed as we swerved up a hill and the roads twisted and thrust us like a dust devil across the island. I started to sweat and drool again, but I was too afraid to pace. After several wheel-spinning curves later, a crunching noise and finally the car lurched to a stop. I knew it. The cabin again.

Something was wrong, though. It smelled like our stinky little cabin, but why was there a fence? It explained why I was looking at a gate, but I was all mixed up. Out of the car, through the gate, fighting the leash tugging at my harness, I minced my way toward the stairs leading to the safety deck. Slam, slam, slam, car doors and then the gate, open and shut, and the leash and harness were off. Really? I scrambled up the stairs to the safety deck. There's a new gate and what is that? It looks like a doghouse disguised as stack of scrap plywood. Seriously. Another gate secured the far end of the safety deck, replacing the Golden Fence. More importantly, the doors to the cabin were all closed. Harrumph. A door slid open and the Farm Manager hustled out with bowls of water, potatoes and apples, hay and grain, and my potty bowl. In and out she went with dizzying speed. This time she had water for my potty bowl. Then she was in and out again with milk. Now we're talking!

It was August, the best month we have here in the Pacific Northwest, and so I wasn't surprised that we were outdoors all day. The Farm Manager coaxed me off the security deck into the newly fenced yard. The long grasses tickled my tummy as I explored and tasted, but there was still a strong deer odor everywhere. The yard had not been fenced long. Could the deer still enter the yard? What about other unpleasant beasts? Why hadn't I been invited indoors yet? The wading pool was lifted off the top of the car and filled with water. I stepped in, plopped over, and relaxed. I got so chill that I pooped in it. Nuts!

As the day progressed, I noticed that the main activity was indoors, while I was barricaded outdoors. I still had my sorry dog shack, which was now stuffed with blankets, toys, and my white rabbit rug. My potty bowl was outdoors, as were my water-potato/apple-hay-and-grain bowls. As the sun went down, the Farm Manager again slipped in and out of the sliding door, and the bedtime milk bowl was added to my collection. For crying out loud, it was bedtime, but we were ten thousand miles away from home, I was about to get eaten alive by wild rogue deer, and no one was going to let me in that door. The best part of being at the cabin had been my own couch. I gazed through the glass slider at the wild party going on indoors and noticed how tiny my little couch had become. I wasn't allowed indoors at night at home, either, dagnabbit. Ignored and abandoned, I skulked off to my pathetic puppy den to await certain death.

Unlike predators, prey animals live in a constant state of alert. Our survival depends upon our ability to recognize danger and to act on it: fight or flight. Capybaras are decidedly cowardly, and I, personally, always opt for flight. Every noise at the cabin was unknown, the weird weather patterns, the salt in the air, the doors that slid open and shut, it was all very disconcerting. The sun rose in the sky the next day, though, my morning milk appeared as usual, and the Farm Manager walked me around the creepy yard once more. She tricked me into my harness, we paraded through the gate, I leapt up into the car and The Bartender drove us away. Where next? Will this nightmare never end?

As the car re-entered the gaping orifice of the gigantic boat, my stomach began to flip-flop in anticipation of the churning, grinding, roiling journey. To my great relief, the crossing was calm. This time, the car was parked in a major pedestrian thoroughfare where millions of people passed outside my window. Some would glance in, startle, shake their heads and move along. Others would stop to talk or ask rude questions such as "Is that a wombat?" My favorite was the father and little boy. The dad passed quickly, but the boy stared into the window, beaming as he recognized my innate royalty. He excitedly called out to his dad "Come here, take a look at this!" Dad took a couple retreating steps, glanced into the car, pronounced me to be a dog and hurried along. The Farm Manager threw the kid a big smile and a thumbs-up. The kid smiled back and happily hurried off.

Summer days at the Funny Farm passed in lazy mode; swimming in the back yard; grazing in the front yard; visitors, lawn mowers, and walks to the mailbox. (Kidding.) Suddenly interrupted by the subtle click of the leash on my harness, I found myself again walking all the way past Gate #1 to the car. I slammed on my brakes as I realized what was packed into the car. Again with the dog crate jam-packed with the Farm Manager's clothes. Yes, there were my blankets, my pirate bed, my white rabbit rug, a cooler full of people food, a milk bucket full of corn and potatoes, and the cotton pickin' barrier behind the front seats. Hmmm.

Not this again.

Sure enough, the drive was long enough that we could have gone to the vet and back a couple times. Then we stopped for a while, but you know, I've never really liked ice cream. Why doesn't the Farm Manager buy me some dandelion greens? All of a sudden The Bartender drove into the mouth of that boat again. I was already sweating bullets, as they say, from the car ride. I pace and drool and sweat so much in the car that I have to shake off the damp, but this boat thing is a hundred times worse. I'm big, so after I shake, the interior surface of the car windows is speckled with . . . well, what is it? I'm always kind of grubby and dusty, so the sweat—which, by the way, smells like capybara urine, but saltier—well, that junk mixes with the dirt to make a kind of organic concrete. So that's on the windows. It's actually everywhere, but you can only tell that by looking at the windows. Sometimes I rub against the windows and add a smeary accent to the spots. There's green drool everywhere from the romaine she feeds me as a distraction, and I stepped in something brown and now I'm pacing again. The Farm Manager is relieved that she sits in the back with me, and the poor Bartender is spinning the toy wheel again up there beyond the barrier, all by his lonesome, concentrating on a fascinating NPR broadcast. I give the Farm Manager a big green kiss and try to step onto her lap.

There's a serious slowing, a swerve to the left, crunchy crunch sounds, and a final swerve to the left. The Farm Manager un-clicked her harness, fumbled at the door, swung it open, leapt out and slammed it in my face! The Bartender leisurely turned off the car from his protective cage and watched as the Farm Manager ran around to the gate, opened it, raced back to the car, opened the door, grabbed my leash and breathlessly invited me to disembark. No way, José!

The Bartender casually glanced over his shoulder at the back seat. He hasn't much sense of smell, so he did a double-take when he saw me among the carnage. He sighed, slid out of the front seat, opened the door to the back, reached through and poked me in the tuchis. I shot out of the car like puffed rice from a cannon! The Farm Manager scampered me through the gate and paused to let me gather my wits. The deer stink wasn't as potent as before and the rabbit activity had slackened as well. The damp salty smell was still strong but the wild animal encroachment had clearly subsided since our last visit.

The cabin was warm and inviting. *Hah!* Joking! I didn't get inside this trip either. I could hear the Farm Manager indoors, opening blinds and windows, turning on the heat, running out the door holding her nose, dropping bulgy plastic bags out the door. One by one my empty bowls were hastily dropped onto the deck in their usual places. I stared in through the sliding door, and jumped when she suddenly rounded the corner behind me. Her arms were overflowing with my

The wading pool is pristine if you ignore the floaters.

blankets, but she sprinted past me and dumped them into the ersatz dogshack. I wandered over to check it out. I went to work marking my blankets and bunching up my white rabbit rug. Chickadees hollered from spruce branches above me. A Steller's Jay hopped from branch to branch on the awkward craggy maple that stretches from the cabin to the street below. The sliding door briskly opened and slammed shut and the Farm Manager set out tea and crumpets for us. Joking again. It was my milk.

The yard was still fenced, the gate was shut, the wild animal smell was stale, but the cabin is not my territory. The Farm Manager accompanied me as I meandered and marked the yard, eating the tall grass and munching on seed heads. She dumped out the leaves and spiders and filled my wading pool with water. I obediently stood in it but I was too nervous to relax and loll about like I did when I was a baby, you know, a month ago when we were here last time. A dog would probably love the cabin and would be running laps around the yard in crazed abandon. I am more like a pampered pet rabbit, and being alone in this strange garden terrified me. I wanted to hide inside the cabin, preferably behind the Farm Manager, or at least within sight of her.

The food bowls filled and emptied, the milk came and went, and the sun dropped low in the sky. I realized that, once again, I would be sleeping in my puppy love-shack. This was not much different from my bed at home, which was also under the stars. The unfamiliar bed seemed to look up at different stars though. I had survived it last time, but I wasn't convinced that the cabin's safety deck was truly secure. I sat outside the sliding door, enviously watching the wild party that was the nightly routine of the Farm Manager and my nemesis, The Bartender. The Farm Manager paced back and forth in the kitchen, cupboards opening, steam rising from pots on the stove. The Bartender sat on the couch, staring at a stack of papers, every once in a while turning a page. The Farm Manager stopped occasionally to flash a light at me, "taking a picture" as she calls it. Interested enough for random photography, but not enough to invite me in for cocoa and marshmallows. She came out a few times to sit with me under those stars and tried to convince me that they were the same ones at home. I followed her to the other door and invited myself in, but she slipped past me and didn't come back out. I went back to the glass sliding door. I sat and stared, and when the lights went off in the cabin, I schlepped my sorry self back to the canine night palace. I pulled the dad-gummed blankets on top of me, and waited for the grim reaper to come calling.

When my morning milk appeared at the regular time, it was reassuring. Lying awake the night before, it had occurred to me that this might be our new house. What if we never went home? Is this it? Do we live here, now? When I was a baby, I used to think that about car rides: that we lived in a car now. But then with the car, it seemed temporary and we had always gotten out again. This felt different. I was confused. I still refused to leave the safety deck without the Farm Manager. The situation was so very perplexing.

That day turned out to be a lot like the day before, but without the car ride. The Farm Manager escorted me around the yard as I tasted the briny weeds, sniffed at the desecrated wading pool (who did that?), and chewed on the blackberry bushes. The sun traced its long lazy summer arc in the sky and I resigned myself to my new home and my funky dog-hovel. Suddenly, the activity level picked up and The Bartender started carrying armfuls of detritus out to the car. The Farm Manager gathered up my bowls and blankets, and those went, too. Nothing they did ever quite made sense, but this was insane. This was the time of day to settle in for the night, not pick up and move camp!

The Farm Manager approached with my harness. Was this a sick joke? I turned and walked away, but she followed. I kept moving, but so did she. I was cornered, but slipped by. The Bartender approached and I panicked. They had me cornered and I clicked. Sometimes I quietly click when I get a piece of corn stuck in my teeth, kind of a Dammit remark. This was not the dammit kind of clicking, it was the *Get Out Of My Way I'm Hopping Mad* clicking. And then I head-butted the Farm Manager. We were off the safety deck and into the garden, now. The Bartender approached and I clicked and head-butted him, too!

The head-butt is a serious act of aggression. It is the precursor to a bite, without the actual bite. When capybaras bite, we come at our terrified victim with our lower teeth. Take a moment to put this book down and move your jaw. Your lower jaw moves up and down, and your eyes keep looking straight forward. Your head doesn't do the moving, that would be crazy, right? It is your hinged jaw that does the moving. Mine is like that, too. So when I bite you, my lower jaw is doing the biting work, my teeth come up from below. When I head butt you, I come straight at you, teeth first, just in case I have to bite you, too. That's how The Bartender and Farm Manager compared matching bruises that night. They both had a big circular background bruise from my big blockhead with upper and lower incisor accents arrayed above and below. It looked like they had pulled giant land leeches off their upper thighs. But there had been no bites. Also, there was no harness around my royal chest.

The Farm Manager and The Bartender consequently decided to spend one more night at the cabin. The Bartender unloaded the car, the Farm Manager schlepped my blankets and white rabbit rug back to the dognobbit hut, and my bedtime milk arrived by magic carpet. They went back inside the cabin, the Farm Manager did her pacing thing in the kitchen, and they ate dinner in silence. They refused to acknowledge the werewolf who stared at them from outside the sliding glass door. The werewolf finally skulked off to the werewolf den, pulled the blankets over his big werebutt, curled up around the white rabbit rug and fell asleep.

I awoke the next morning to discover The Bartender in full offense mode, nostrils flaring, size fifteen's prancing like a demented prehistoric boxer. I shook the sleep from my eyes as I heard the harness click into place. I guessed we were going home. Funny thing is, when I think about it, we never went back to the cabin. Why the Sam Hill[22] not?

---

22   In the early 1900's, Sam Hill designed and built the roads that connected Eastern Washington to the Pacific coast. At the time, everybody thought he was insane for insisting that the roads could be engineered and successfully built. We invoke his name when we make "impossible" plans or act crazy.

THE THEFT

A long time ago I wrote a series of blog posts[23] about a memorable trip to the veterinary clinic. I can't believe how innocent I was back then. Here's the story, but in hindsight (get it?) I might be compelled to add a few details.

Part One—The Anticipation

I'm going to the vet clinic today, even though Gari's[24] vet from the ROUS Foundation came to visit me on Tuesday. Maybe Dr. F wants to look at the scar on my face.

I've never had my milk in the car before and I don't usually get it this early, either! This is going to be a very special day! We were exactly on time and I got right out of the car on my new ramp and pranced into the clinic, making my best happy noises! After getting weighed I decided to take a nap. This is way too early in the day for me! But it turned out we had to walk back to an examining room. Whatever, I can always walk down there a little bit later, right after we all stop in the hall so somebody can please scratch this spot– right there under my chin. All righty then, everything's good, scar looks awesome, let's go home!

But we weren't going to go home at all. I tried to bite a hole in the seat cushion, but it was hard to do with The Farm Manager's jacket there. I smeared some mustache milk on the chair back instead. SO bored! Gee, thanks for the great new toy. Was that in your purse? Isn't that a mobile for babies? It does dangle nicely and I do like to bite the dragonfly. In the future, stick with those chubby stuffed IKEA rats. Now I have something in my eye. It's a towel, that's why I tossed it. Who's asking? Can we get out of here, please? Ugh. I'm glad we all brought books to read. Mine is Capyboppy and I am reading the part where he gets sick. I'm getting a little anxious, now. I know you have been cleaning the floor with that towel but I'm sweating bullets here and I need a blanket!

Wait! Ouch! What was that? When did Dr. F sneak in here! Come back, I have some questions! Zzzzzzzzzzzz.

---

23 These were posted on the Dobby the Capybara blog, www.petcapybara.com back in 2011.
24 Garibaldi Rous was a capybara Facebook friend of mine. We used to write stories together. Coincidentally, he was adopted by Melanie after my brother Caplin died.

Part Two—The Theft

Truthfully, I don't remember any of this next part. I am relying on the Farm Manager's faulty memory while ignoring her tendency to exaggerate.

She watched everything and took photos through a little window.

She told me two vet techs carried me away down the hall. Then, the veterinarians took my harness off and decided where to connect their assorted paraphernalia before they flipped me onto my back. They strapped me down and Dr. M. put an oxygen mask on me. They connected me to intravenous fluids. Subcutaneous fluids are not a good idea for capybaras because of the weird way our skin is attached. (The fluid makes a balloon that expands and almost blows up.) Dr. M had to hold my hand the whole time so I wouldn't get scared. Actually, holding it up helped to keep the fluids flowing into me. Dr. F took a good long look at my nether regions, poking and prodding at my personal equipment. It took him a very long time to prepare my private parts for surgery. The thief, aka Dr. F, cut two holes in me and stole a couple gigantic pieces out of there. He put them into a couple of nice jars, maybe to display in his curio cabinet at home. I guess he couldn't think of any more stuff to take out of me, so Dr. F painstakingly sewed my insides back up. He must have been doing embroidery down there. Then he glued the skin back together to hide the holes. I got a couple nice souvenir bandages. There was even a pink one with red hearts where they drew a blood sample. But we weren't through yet.

Garibaldi's Radiographs

Dr. F and his assistant carried my snoozing carcass back down another hall, hoisted me off the stretcher, and plunked me down on the x-ray table. Dr. M hurriedly followed us down the hall because the oxygen and the IV fluids were still attached. My vital signs were monitored during all of the procedures. Nobody trusts me to hold still unless they knock me out, so it's kind of a big deal even to take radiographs.

This part of the ordeal was a special gift to my adopted brother and friend, Garibaldi Rous. You see, Gari's hind legs don't look right, and we're pretty sure mine are normal. Gari is a little knock-kneed and I am almost bow-legged! The Farm Manager thinks I walk with a John Wayne swagger. I don't think so, it's my own special rumblestrut.[25] Anyway, a few weeks ago, Gari had radiographs taken of his hindquarters, but there are no radiographs of a normal capybara to compare them to. I supplied the normal (control) radiographs, but they had to try to get exactly the same angles as Gari's radiographs.

Of course, I held perfectly still for these ground-breaking radiographs, hah hah hah. Dr. F finally gave me another injection. There were so many pokings the Farm Manager can't remember what all of them were. I'm not scared to get shots, though, even when I'm fully awake. This injection happened to be my wake-up shot.

---

25   When guinea pig boars (dudes) show off for the girls, they do a silly hopping dance accompanied by an irresistible song. The guinea pig sows (honeys) are the only ones who don't think they look ridiculous.

When I woke up, the Farm Manager held me and sang silly songs. The Bartender helped Dr. F carry my deadweight back to the room where it all started. Dr. F said I weighed more after the surgery, even though it seems like I should have weighed less! There was one more injection and then a long wait for me to stand up! Some brown stuff fell out of my butt, and the examination room wasn't very clean by the time we high-tailed it out of there. It seems like Dr. F should have taken that brown junk out when he had the chance.

The big surprise from my radiographs is that at 2-1/2 years old, I am still growing! The Farm Manager and I donated my radiographs to the ROUS Foundation. We hope they will help everyone understand what is wrong with Gari's butt.[26]

Part Three—The Recovery

When I arrived home from the veterinary clinic I was more than a little woozy but it didn't hurt to sit down or anything. Plus, I can sort of remember what happened, so I don't have to ask the Farm Manager. I was too indisposed to write it up at the time, so this is an after-the-fact accounting.

I wanted to climb up into my bed but I couldn't drag myself up a step that big...plus, I was staggering around a little when I walked. Drunk as a skunk, as they say, and better off keeping low to the ground. I went back into the kitchen and stared at my potato bowl. I was much too groggy to eat my corn and apple. I did a lot of self-evaluation during this time, deep contemplation about the state of the universe. The Farm Manager would probably say that I spent a lot of time staring off into space, but that is projection on her part. She has little appreciation of my capacity for introspection.

As the afternoon progressed, I began to appreciate my situation. It couldn't get much better than this: my White Rabbit Rug, my "sleep in the house" bed, my frog blanket, and a bowl of milk! This was the royal treatment I deserved. And then I fell asleep, right there in the kitchen.

---

26   What about those radiographs? Sadly, it turned out that Gari had a very unfortunate bone density problem. Not only did he walk funny, but his head bone was not dense enough to properly hold his teeth in position. This was all due to very poor nutrition when he was growing up. We don't know much about his childhood, but we don't think he had ever been outdoors before Melanie adopted him at 10 months old. He probably never even had milk. You can read about his story at http://www.gianthamster.com/, but it is too sad for this book.

The next day, The Chambermaid put some blankets on the deck so I could comfortably receive visitors. Celery the hen shared some birdseed with me, and Wiley Wabbit dropped by to say hello, too. I think he was looking for stray pieces of lettuce and corn. I didn't even have to get out of bed at milk time. The bowl was delivered to my bedside.

I spent most of the next two days right there on the deck. In fact, the stairs were blocked, so I wouldn't hurtle myself into the abyss. All in all, I slept in the kitchen for three nights! It was glorious, though I think The Bartender was slipping something into my milk to keep me quiet and drowsy.

Four days later, the barricades disappeared from the deck steps. The Farm Manager reduced the dosage on the pain medication so I wasn't as sleepy. I ventured out to inventory my various projects. I checked the aviary and visited my friends. I got pouffy for my hens. I got pouffy for my medicine. I got pouffy because it was a sunny day. I checked on my private pasture under the apple tree in the back yard. Fences keep the destructive chickens out and I was relieved to see that only squirrels had trespassed in there. Hens scratch all the grass away and turn it into a mud hole for the ducks who finish the work by dabbling holes everywhere. All was well.

Five days later I had a little picnic with my friends Pamplemousse the hen, and two outrageous Muscovy drakes we took in, Julian and Romeo. There must have been a problem with the swimming pool because the steps were fenced off. Oh well, I wasn't completely healed up yet. Wiley Wabbit kept coming into my pen, so I had to remind him whose territory it was.

And a couple days later everything was back to normal. The swimming pool was open, I was grazing afternoons in the front yard, and the bedside service had become sketchy. Oh well.

Chapter Four

WHAT'S FOR BREAKFAST?

Everybody asks what I eat and if I could speak I'd probably say something shocking like "little children" or "caviar" or "well-aged dirty socks." The Farm Manager speaks for me and she is very boring and says "grass." I'm writing this memoir, though, and so I'll tell you that it depends. When I was little I drank lots of milk. I ate my hay, my grain, grass, corn, and my vegetables. I even ate fruit. I am a lot like human children, though, and soon decided that to eat such a variety was silly when all I really wanted was the milk and the corn. That has been my goal for eight years now, to get it pared down to the essentials.

Grazing is pleasant, though, and my afternoons in the front yard pasture are kind of a capybara dream come true. We have a lot of rough grass, even some sedges and rushes that are wetland plants like the vegetation I would probably eat in the wild. Some of our grass gets six feet tall if I don't chew it down, so this isn't your typical golf course putting green. It's full of bugs and my favorite dandelions so I know it's safe to eat. The coolest grass in the front yard is called bamboo. You might be thinking that I eat those woody yellow stick things, but our bamboo grows as a bushy green hedge, and I eat the leaves. When the grass stops growing in winter, the bamboo is still thick and green, so it's essential cold weather forage for capybaras, even wild ones.

Baby me ate all sorts of things that seem crazy now. I ate Cheerios,™ Kix,™ and shredded wheat, for instance. I ate it mixed in with guinea pig pellets and rolled oats, kind of a capy granola. I would try anything like potato chips, pretzels, tortilla chips, all sorts of people food, but I didn't really like it much, not compared to grass. Gradually, I stopped eating anything from my grain bowl, and the Farm Manager got rid of everything but the guinea pig food and oats. She also has snuck in something called Equine Senior,® which sounds suspiciously like horse food, which it can't possibly be. Anyway, I carefully eat the oats out of the bowl and leave all the pellety things behind.

Fruit was one of my first rejections. I don't eat any of it. All that melon, strawberries, banana-like squishy stuff, forget about it. I'll eat banana chips, though, especially if they come out of a crinkly bag. I also eat pears, especially those tiny green crunchy ones, but none of those rotten squishy ones. Apples are okay, too, especially in August when they fall from the sky. The back yard fills up with apples, mostly underneath that tree back there. It's an automatic buffet. The squirrels and I wander and nibble all day long, until the apples are gone.

There's one more important food group to consider: coprophages. You can go look that up, but I'll tell it to you again: capybaras eat their own poop! Now

before you toss this book away in disgust, I want to tell you that some very cute and dainty looking animals eat their own poop: guinea pigs, chinchillas, and rabbits! Of course, everyone knows that guinea pigs are completely disgusting creatures, maybe even more despicable than capybaras. However, rabbits have a very good reputation. They are as charming and dignified as poodles. And they eat their own poop. So if you are going to judge, keep in mind that some very fine representatives of the animal kingdom eat their own poop, and that you should prop up your animal prejudices with some other dubious data.

In fact, I am very dainty about my poop-eating. It is generally a morning occupation and I require privacy. Because I devour it directly from my tuchis,[27]

---

27 Seriously, you should be able to guess this one from context. Butt, yes.

I end up sitting in kind of a twisted pretzel shape, leaving me quite vulnerable to Jaguars and Anacondas. Imagine you are sitting on your front lawn, front legs spread wide, your head is between your spread back legs, you can already picture how awkward it is. Then a big eagle swoops over your head and you fall over. So embarrassing. That's why I prefer a quiet nook under cover, no observers, soft music, condiments like blanket fringe. Do you recall that I mentioned pancakes? Imagine that halfway through your breakfast you feel a nap coming on. Flop down onto the blankets for a snooze. Wake up an hour later, sit up, and what is *that?* Oops, flat breakfast. AKA pancakes.

SNACK TIME: MY SIX SWIMMING POOLS

The Farm Manager was smart enough to turn her nose up at baby pools, the cute little inflatable ones. My teeth haven't always been this big, but they were razor sharp from the beginning. She did buy one of those "pool in a box" with rigid sides that roll up into a small shelf-sized package. Those are terrific fun because you can push the side over and let the water whoosh out! Most people don't know how exciting it is to bite the bottom of those pools! They are made of the thinnest plastic possible. One tiny nip and you can tear open the bottom like a can of sardines! It's great for the lawn, too. Keeps it nice and green.

I'm a bit sentimental about the next pool. I should say pools, because right now, eight years later, I still have a dozen of them, in two sizes. Some are blue and some are purple but they are all hard plastic and have a fish or octopus design stamped on the inside. Plastic molded wading pools are stackable, so as the edge gets ~~chewed~~ worn out, you can fix it by strategic stacking. By now, some of mine are three-ply. Most have been scrubbed out so many times that the octopus are like cinqtopus, and the purple is barely lavender, but they still hold water.

When I was little the small ones were perfect and I could almost swim in them. The baby size is easy to dump and refill so those are still in use around here. My hot tub is a small molded plastic wading pool. I can get totally wet if I roll over in it or if the Farm Manager stands there and dips warm water over me, the preferred bathing technique. When the water is nice and clean and the sun heats it up, they are perfect Big Boy potty pools. The Farm Manager is never shocked when she discovers this, because she loves surprises. Clean pool surprises are especially nice.

The bigger pools are tricky to dump and take a long time to refill, so they only seem to come into use during emergencies. They magically appear when my "real" swimming pool is off limits, or when we have new ducks, serious emergencies like that. Mostly, they are upside down in funny places, like big umbrellas. They are like Chicken Astrodomes, keeping the minions dry.

When the big wading pools first arrived, they became awesome waterfall pools. Set into the hillside, the water overflowed from one into another and it was very cool. Except they were in the aviary, and I only have occasional access to

that area. I'll never know why my pools were in there, but it certainly made it awkward for me to swim. I had to wait for the Farm Manager to let me in, and then, you know, I don't do my business in the aviary. Sometimes I had to stand at the gate, legs crossed, for *minutes* before I was let out to the back yard potty area. Those big pools in the aviary were great, but they have been replaced by the ridiculous tin can pool. I'll tell you about that later. Anyway, the ducks seem to like it, but what do they know?

My first Big Boy swimming pool came from end-of-the-season sales at a local department store. It sat in a box for a while and then presto-chango, it was a pool! The most glorious pool in the world! About fifteen feet across and almost four feet deep, it might have been the Pacific Ocean to baby me. I was scared of it at first, because everything new is scary. There were these huge straw steps to climb, and then invisible water, so much of it. From the ground, it was a gigantic wall, an obstacle that also created a hiding area behind it. I loved that pool, though, and it lasted a really long time.

What makes a pool cheap? The sale price or the technique they chose to manufacture the seams? Amidst all the documented damage to prior and subsequent pools, the demise of this particular pool cannot be attributed to me. When the Farm Manager states, for instance, that I "ate six pools" she is lying. The freeze and thaw of winter had probably been too much for the heat-sealed seams. By the end of the following summer, the leaking was steady and the end was near.

Fortunately, the same model pool was still available, though the not-on-sale price wasn't as attractive. Out with the old, in with the new! Here we can insert that apt cliché "easier said than done." These are large pools. They hold about 5,000 gallons of water. And my goldfish are swimming in that water. You can't catch my frisky fish until the water is almost totally siphoned out, so that is the first step: set up hoses to drain the water. Then we watch for Great Blue Herons and keep an eyeball on the water level to make sure we don't leave my fish friends high and dry. Then the Farm Manager and The Bartender hop in there and catch the fish. Due to their gross incompetence, that takes all afternoon, and involves buckets, nets, and lots of naughty language. We get to find out whether there are any holes in the Farm Manager's boots and how many goldfish The Bartender accidentally bails overboard, the proverbial "baby out with the bathwater" disorder.

Then there are the straw bale steps. They deserve their own chapter, but let's say that they don't last too long. At any given time, the steps are rotten, listing to one side, a gap opens up near the top, creating an ideal situation for breaking a clumsy rodent leg. Get that garbage outta here! The saturated straw weighs a ton, and so needs to be disposed of "here." Seriously, getting six rotten bales of straw out of the back yard is not easy. So let's find a final resting place for this lovely compost, okay?

How big is your garbage can? Do you have space for a dozen metal supports plus the in-between structure and a gigantic rubberized fabric pool the size of your car? We do! (puffs out chest, bragging) The very good news is that the fantastic amount of work The Bartender and the Farm Manager put into creating a level compacted base for the previous pool was intact and preserved. The "under-pool" looked like a great big gingersnap cookie.

The Farm Manager and The Bartender joked about buying pools in bulk at Costco, and that would have been a great idea this time. It was too early in the summer to find a pool on sale, so they paid full price for Swimming Pool #2. Even after the first pool failed, they still bought the same brand. There really isn't much of a selection, though, and no one was silly enough to suggest the big pools with inflatable sides. Razor-sharp teeth.

They drained the pool, watching for herons, played a round of "Catch the Goldfish," bailed the water, nabbed the fish they missed on the first round, and hauled the pool supports and plastic liner out to the garbage. Then they hauled in the new pool, spread it out, wrestled it onto the fifteen foot diameter gingersnap cookie, and filled it up with minimal shenanigans, barely glancing at the instructions. Swimming Pool #2 was thereby installed. Then the straw bale steps went up, the goldfish were re-installed, but I was suspicious of the invisible water and stared at it for three days before swimming in it.

Remember how I mentioned that they should have bought the pools in bulk? That's because Swimming Pool #2 began to leak the very first day. Like a moth to a flame, the Farm Manager and The Bartender had run out and bought the very same model pool as a replacement. They still had the receipts and the store had agreed to give them a replacement, so even if they had wanted to try a different brand, they would probably still have taken the replacement and set it up. But they were wary, now. The new favorite topic was swimming pools, but the future looked grim.

They drained pool #2, watched for herons, played a round of "Catch the Goldfish," bailed the water, nabbed the fish they missed on the first round, hauled the pool supports and plastic liner out to the driveway. They carefully folded and crammed the soggy pool, the supports, and fistfuls of miscellaneous hardware into the original carton. Hefting the raunchy, leaking box into the back of the Subaru, they made the trek back to the store to exchange pools. Back at the ranch, they hauled in Swimming Pool #3: The Replacement. They threw away the instructions, spread it out, wrestled it onto the 15' diameter gingersnap cookie, and filled it up with 5,000 gallons of city tap water. The straw bale steps went up, the goldfish were re-installed, and I was suspicious and stared at the invisible water for two days before swimming.

There were many swimming pool discussions, and after a month or two, the subject began to include filtering and steps. The Farm Manager began to speak openly about fantasies of in-ground pools with waterfalls and spas, basking ledges and serious filtering. With winter groundwater levels at an inch above ground, permanent in-ground swimming pools act like concrete boats, popping out of the ground and floating like miraculous arks. Small pumps and filters, biofilters, bigger pumps, pre-filters, UV filters, chlorine? Wood steps, platforms, modified children's play structures, ramps, and back to straw bales. There is no better dinner conversation topic than capybara swimming pools and their accoutrements.

Next time, it was almost six months before the leaking started. At first, the Farm Manager added water as usual, casually inspecting the periphery for, well, I don't know what. She was definitely suspicious, though. The water was green, again, and it wasn't possible to observe my submarine activities. I had developed a fun new swimming technique where I pushed off the side of the pool, bouncing everything around. I can get up some pretty good speed if I want to. The Farm Manager was having to add more and more water. The refill hose was in place, more-or-less permanently, now.

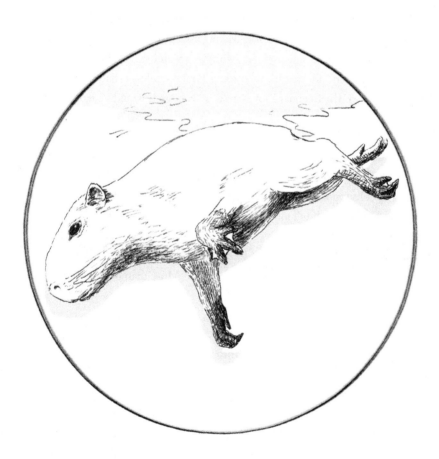

Take her down!

One day the Farm Manager was behind the pool, tossing my noodles and toys back up into the pool but it was taking way too long. There was an eerie silence followed by a wail. "Oh no!" the Farm Manager said. Then she said a whole bunch of other stuff and she was looking right at me, but I had never ever heard those words before, and I actually have a pretty fair vocabulary, for a rodent, anyway.

I think it is pretty cool that I can bite a hole in a swimming pool from the inside. The dainty little waterfalls on the outside are so pretty, like little fairy falls. They make fantastic mud, too. I was so excited about my handiwork that I wrote a blog post about it! The Farm Manager was not nearly so enthusiastic. The waterfalls were increasing and the swimming water was draining out at an alarming rate. I wasn't allowed in Swimming Pool #3 unless it had been refilled within a day or so. The freeboard[28] was getting so large it would be hard for me to get out.

One day, they drained pool #3, watched for herons, played a round of "Catch the Goldfish," bailed the water, nabbed the fish they missed on the first round, hauled the pool supports and plastic liner out to the garbage. They hauled in Swimming Pool #4. It didn't look anything like the first three swimming pools. Instead of one big fat box, there were a bunch of boxes, mostly long and skinny, but some squished flat ones, too. The Bartender rummaged around in the boxes until he found the instruction booklet. A booklet! More than one piece of paper, this was a serious tome.

The Farm Manager and The Bartender stared at the instructions for a really, really long time. This pool required a reinforced foundation. The old pools had effectively compacted the ground beneath them and it was solid and nearly level. Installing new pools had been a snap. Swimming Pool #4 was a prima donna: it had to have little blocks under its supports, they had to be impeccably spaced on a perfectly level perimeter. A perimeter that was 16' diameter, not 15'. A small difference, but it meant adding compacted material in a 6" swath outside the existing almost-level but 15' diameter gingersnap cookie. Furthermore, it

---

28 That's the distance from the water to the top edge of the pool.

required a soft soil berm inside the base of the perimeter. They had to frost that cookie with dirt.

I hate to go for car rides, but it would be worth it to go to Home Depot. Some of my garden came from there and I fantasize about taste-testing the plants before they come home. The real problem is that there is never room for a capybara in the back of the Subaru after a trip to Home Depot. This trip will go down in history: a dozen concrete steps and three dozen bags of potting soil. Swimming Pool #4 turned out to be more expensive than they thought. Plus, the old pools would have been filling by now. The Farm Manager and The Bartender were at the end of Day #1 with nothing more to show for it than a severely overloaded vehicle with suspiciously misshapen tires.

The next day they installed the gingersnap cookie extension. They set out the concrete step foundation blocks, the bottom rail connectors, the bottom rail, and wrestled the pool sidewall out of its box. This was a *metal-sided* pool. Genius, right? The aluminum sidewall was like the biggest, most treacherous roll of toilet paper imaginable. Sharp edges, sproingy-ness beyond comprehension, it was coiled up so snugly that you would have had a hard time slipping a pencil down the center. So tight! It made a spooky sound, not quite musical, more like it was groaning in pain from the unrolling. It weighed as much as the Subaru. I watched in horror as it tried to eat the Farm Manager and The Bartender while they slipped the bottom of the roll into the teeny tiny groove in the 16' diameter bottom rail. It was frightening. The toilet paper kept moaning as it wrapped itself around the Farm Manager and then The Bartender. A dachshund would have barked his silly head off, but capybaras are stoic. We are prey animals, and watching one of our own consumed like a canapé, well, that's life.

"They slipped the bottom of the roll into the teeny tiny groove..." That is the funniest line I have written so far. Where are the videos of that? There was a teeny tiny groove, but there was no slipping into. As one of them would slip the wall into the groove, it would pop right out where the other one stood. They played that game for a while and then tossed the sidewall into the shrubbery and had a "discussion." It wasn't as loud as an argument, but it pushed the definition of polite conversation right to the edge of the herd.

They finally came up with a method that probably wasn't included in the instructions. They slipped the leading edge of the roll of the sidewall into the channel and the Farm Manager held it into the channel as tightly as possible while The Bartender unfurled and embedded the roll until it threatened to snap at him. Then they called over a third helper, and I'll call him "Ladder Number One." Using duct tape and bungee cords, they replaced the Farm Manager with Ladder Number One. The Farm Manager in turn replaced The Bartender at his station, and The Bartender inched his way around the perimeter, stuffing the malicious toilet paper into the channel, the Farm Manager centimetering behind him (she's much smaller) until they reached the halfway mark. At this point, they called in reinforcements, and I'll call this fourth helper "Ladder Number Two." Again with the duct tape and bungee cords, they inched and centimetered around to the end. Or maybe it was the beginning, again. Of course, the ends met up perfectly. It's simple math really, isn't it? Listen, 16' diameter pool, the channel is by definition 50.27'. The ends are designed to overlap so that you can easily slip the rivets into the pre-drilled holes. Shockingly, the alignment fell somewhat short of perfect. Let us say that this next "discussion" was not as adversarial, but it was louder and more *unified against* Swimming Pool #4, which was already top choice for The Most Hated Swimming Pool, *ever*.

The next step was much simpler. They simply hopped over the sidewall (without jarring it out of the bottom channel, or should we call it the butt-head channel?) and spread the potting soil around the inside edge of the sidewall. Seriously, this was the easy part. Made a bit more difficult because helpers Number One and Number Two were already occupied elsewhere. How many ladders do YOU have? How would you hop over that 42" high sidewall into the "pool?" And then, of course, if you are a "planning ahead" type, how do you get out? There were no helpful tips in the instructions and the Farm Manager and The Bartender began to wonder if anyone had ever successfully assembled one of these behemoths.

The next step was beyond my wildest dreams! They brought in the "liner." This was the most delicious pool, ever! The sidewalls were metal, but there was a plastic liner! How perfect! Well, not quite perfect, because in order for the liner to stretch and "relax" the temperatures would have to be around 70°F degrees. (21°C degrees). So funny! This is the Pacific Northwest! We only get temperatures above 70 degrees about twice a year! Well, maybe more than that, but this was not August! It was May. The liner would not stretch all the way around the pool, the day was too cool. We were in luck, though. The next day the sun came out and they had that sucker stretched the full perimeter of the pool! That was the only bit of good luck they had installing Swimming Pool #4.

Once the liner had relaxed and could be coaxed into place, they opened the final two boxes, assembled a bunch of handsome struts, some sturdy top edge reinforcement, and the stunningly decorative top rail. Swimming Pool #4 was almost ready.

The Farm Manager had another brilliant idea. The straw bale steps were becoming an expensive maintenance proposition. She decided that a molded plastic play structure would be a more permanent solution to the entry dilemma posed by a 42" above-ground pool to a 24" tall pet capybara. How does a capybara get up to that structure, though? More straw bale steps, of course! Such a genius. With the addition of the play structure, the steps took up much more space, and the platform at the top was a bit too low. It might have been fine for a steeplechase hurdle but it was supposed to help ease me into the pool, not make it an Olympic event. The Farm Manager stuffed bags with Styrofoam to build the platform up to where I might have a fighting chance getting into the pool. In the end, she managed to create steps so formidable and forbidding that it would be two days before I would climb up there to investigate my new pool. After two days of surveying the invisible water for alligators, I finally made the plunge.[29]

In hindsight, Swimming Pool #4 might have lasted longer had I been more frightened of the monstrous new stairs. If I had waited a few more days, the lifespan of Swimming Pool #4 would have nearly doubled. However, I could see my giddy goldfish frolicking down at the bottom of my new swimming pool, so in I went. I swam around in circles a few times, enjoying the "new pool smell." It

---

29 Watch me dive! *Capybara Training: Olympic Diving*, https://youtu.be/31N0b5PhMCo

was glorious and it was delicious. I took a little nip of the liner, right above the waterline. The Farm Manager blanched, but gamely brought out a roll of duct tape and patched the hole. A scant five days after installation, Swimming Pool #4 was in peril.

Less than a week later, Swimming Pool #4 was completely off limits. If all of my tasting nips had been above the waterline, this might have been the end of the swimming pool story. The very nature of a vinyl liner is that no matter how careful you are, there will be wrinkles. Like a hangnail or a scab, wrinkles call out for abuse. I ask you, could you possibly resist nipping at a wrinkle in your swimming pool? Jeepers creepers, they were everywhere! The bottom of the pool, the seam at the bottom of the wall, even the sidewall area. Little imperfections like pimples to be investigated and destroyed. Eleven days after the grand finale of the excruciating installation, Swimming Pool #4 was doomed, and a "No Entry" barrier was permanently installed on the monstrosity of an entry "experience," that the Farm Manager was still optimistically referring to as "the new stairs." The Bartender's destructive tendencies became indispensable. An ad was put on Craigslist, the pool was disassembled in a nanosecond, and Swimming Pool #4 was no more. A new record for anti-longevity, it hadn't even made it to the 2 week mark.

The prevailing topic of discussion again centered vaguely upon "swimming pool." I listened avidly as waterfalls and basking areas were again discussed. The tantalizing notion of a Jacuzzi spa gained ground. But all that happened was that my wading pools were strewn about the back yard and filled. My goldfish languished in buckets in the bathtub at my throne room, and the giant gingersnap cookie was again exposed to the skies above. Less than one week after Swimming Pool #4 crossed the rainbow bridge, Swimming Pool #5 made an abrupt appearance.

If Swimming Pool #4 had been a mistake, then Swimming Pool #5 was a spectacular fiasco. It was basically an oversized tuna fish can. Surely they were joking! The cacophony of thuds it made as it was offloaded from the feed store delivery truck were a bad omen. I watched in horror as the driver rolled it into the back yard. It narrowly missed taking out the south storage area roof and barreled along, mowing down every blade of grass in its path.

Swimming Pool #5 was an ugly galvanized metal stock tank. A puny 8' diameter, it was a mere 24" tall. Here's the description: "Our galvanized stock tanks feature 20 gauge galvanized bottoms and 21 gauge sides as well as a four-ply double-lock seam at the bottom sealed with Pliogrip adhesive/sealant seam sealer for a superior bond. 1-1/8" top rim is permanently rolled for strong reinforcement. 1" tube inside rim of tank for additional strength. Features a 1" drain plug. Unmatched quality and consistency in construction. Deep sidewall corrugation for strength. Heavy-duty zinc G90 coating withstands harsh weather conditions." And that's the way life was with Swimming Pool #5. It was dull but functional.

It was lonely, too. Other than its friend the Great Blue Heron who started hanging around. I refused to acknowledge that #5 was even a pool. Solid, unforgiving metal sidewalls, absolutely bulletproof bottom, what was this thing, anyway? My straw steps were there, kinda silly because I could hang my head over the edge of the pool. So puny. My goldfish looked cramped and cold, my toys were bumping into each other, and it was so industrial! Like a prison-quality pool. What had I done to deserve this?

After a few days I got in. It was okay, I guess. Then I panicked. *I couldn't get out!* The sides were as tall as a straw bale! A formidable height, there was no way I could jump out. *I was doomed!* I hopped out and refused to go back in. Okay, *right then* I could hop out, but what about later? What if I couldn't get out then?

The Farm Manager stacked concrete steps on the inside so I could make a more graceful exit. I gave it another try. Two more tries, actually, and too scared to remember to poop in it! She floated corn on the cob on a Frisbee to entice me in. She even floated a bowl of milk to try to get me in there. I am *no fool.* That was one creepy pool. I was done. I never went in again.[30]

---

30   Five years later and I have never again been in that pool. It is set up in the aviary for the ducks, and they love it. Fine. They can have it, but I'm never getting into that thing.

I watched with excitement when #5 was moved out. Big enough to be a major pain in the nether regions, they actually had to chop a hole in the aviary roof, hoist the behemoth up, and drop the rigid beast down through the hole to get rid of it. A difficult but successful riddance. The ducks like it, gives you an idea of their opinion. Not too discriminating, but appreciative, I'll give them that.

The best part is that Swimming Pool #6 arrived. It cost about ten times what the first pools cost. That's why it took so long for it to come. First, the Farm Manager had to save the money. Then she had to be certain I wouldn't eat it the first day. There were many soul-searching days. Would I really bite right through the sidewall of a $3000 pool? What if I did? Would the corn stop coming? What about my milk? Would they skimp on my bedtime milk?

Swimming Pool #6 was a Big Deal. My big human brother was here with a ~~bunch of friends~~ work crew, and they had already dispatched the tin can pool. Now they hauled boxes into the back yard and the Farm Manger fenced me off from the fun. The work crew leveled off the chicken scratched gingersnap and expanded it a skoshe. There was a lot of mud from that potting soil left by #4, and by now there were 3 embedded pool covers reinforcing the gingersnap. This swimming pool had yet another set of instructions to ignore. The crew was appreciating the simplicity of #5 at this point. They labored like wild dingoes to put #6 together and, by golly, it was magnificent.

I loved everything about Swimming Pool #6. I loved the old-fashioned straw bale steps, I loved my goldfish, I loved my hula-hoops and my rubber ducky. This time the invisible water wasn't so scary and I dove right in without hesitation. I swam around and around and to the side where the Farm Manager stood and then I took a little nip at the edge of the pool. She made a funny noise and backed away from the pool. The top edge of the pool isn't fancy or anything, it isn't as if I took a chomp out a carved teak railing. It is a stupid metal pipe through a crummy plastic sleeve. My harmless little nip had exposed the metal, the plastic was now a wrinkly tear near the top. I took another nip. The Farm Manager turned red and puffed up her full 5'0" short height.

"Not For Dobby!" said the Farm Manager. The Bartender came running over to look. Such tiny little holes, what was the big deal? I continued to swim and nip, nip and swim. The next day there was black hard plastic corrugated drainline encircling the top of the pool. The reinforced edge wasn't much fun to bite any more, but I still loved Swimming Pool #6. I swam and the water slowly turned green, the fish circled near the bottom, and toys bumped gently against the reinforced edge.

At this writing, Swimming Pool #6 reigns supreme. It has some benign nips to the sides, but you can hardly see them behind the wire fencing that now surrounds the pool. There is a fancy new pump and filter, so it doesn't matter that the pool fills up with 40 mallards each afternoon. The steps are a constant challenge, but for all the talk about replacements, the Farm Manager knows I would treat them with the same respect accorded to Swimming Pool #5: I would never use them.

LUNCHTIME IS AT NOON SHARP!
(AKA DOBBY RULES AND REGULATIONS)

When you rule a Principality, as I do, you get to make the rules. In fact you can have no rules or millions of rules. I'm a little OCD so I have no problem making rules. I make rules about making rules. That's what ruling is all about.

One rule that is difficult for me to enforce is the use of the princely washing machine. I can see the washer/dryer complex from my kitchen territory. From there I can also observe certain people using it for their own clothing! Sometimes they wash guinea pig and rabbit laundry in there, too! I know, that's rude, isn't it? The washer is to be used exclusively for my own royal blankets and bedding. Make a note of it.

Another rule I have is that the Farm Manager is not to leave the house. She is not to get into her fancy-pants sports car and drive away. She does this periodically and when she does, I make a statement on the kitchen floor. She ignores my protest, but I will continue my emphatic poops until she understands that *I need her here at all times.*

My days are complicated, so it is of critical importance to adhere to a strict schedule. Life would become very confusing if the Farm Manager randomly took me to the front yard in the morning, or suddenly gave me my luncheon corn at 11:00 or 1:00, though that has happened a couple times. Here's my corn schedule:

8:30 – 9:00: Morning milk and corn, the variation is dependent upon who serves it. The Bartender is prompt and the Farm Manager is lazy

12:00: Corn, this timing is sacred

3:00 – 4:30: Corn in the front yard, the variation is dependent upon the season

5:30 – 7:30: Bedtime milk and corn, the sun is a tyrant, isn't it?

I sleep outdoors in a secure pen, but my bed is very cozy so I am not eager to get up in the morning. In fact, I often take a nap in the kitchen right after my morning milk. There's no point in rushing through the day. Of course, an astute student of capybara habits will know what I am really doing in my bed in the morning. That's right, I am eating poop! That's when we do it. I don't really mind if the Farm Manager watches, but it is kind of personal so I don't do it around strangers. If you are ever in a relationship with a capybara, that's how you can tell when you're close: they will eat their poop when you're watching. (Ooh! I have a great valentine idea for next year!)

I have more sacred breakfast rituals. First I drink a few sips of milk to make sure it's acceptable. Then I spin around to check on the status of my corn. It is supposed to be available immediately after my milk. I used to share it outside with the squirrels, but we disagree on the concept of "share." I also examine my grain bowl for oats. There is other pelleted nonsense in there, but I painstakingly pick out the oats, then go back to my milk. Breakfast is exhausting, so I take a nap in the kitchen while I wait for the Farm Manager to prepare my potatoes and apples. If it takes too long, I wander out to my bed where I can eat poop while I wait. This explains why the Farm Manager finds "pancakes" in my bed. Imagine what your breakfast would look like if you sat on it!

Speaking of my milk, unspeakable things have happened to it. When I was a baby, I drank my milk from a bottle. It was commercially available powdered goat's milk and it was delicious. That was satisfactory until I started to bite the nipples off the bottle. Suddenly, I was drinking milk from a bowl. That's when my milk began to evolve. The first adulteration was the addition of plain low-fat yogurt. To this day there is yogurt in my milk. It's hard to suck milk out of a bowl, so the next debasement was organic baby rice cereal. That abruptly improved to baby oatmeal after a news report hinted at impurities in baby rice cereal. Baby cereal thickens the milk so it is easier to slurp up but over the years I have perfected a "milk herding" technique. If I swing my snout to the side, a bit of milk washes up into my mouth as it ricochets off the high sidewalls of the milk bowl. I'm quite proud of this method, especially since it swishes the sticky milk all over my nose, turning me into a milky Magic Marker. I can write that milk everywhere: the window, the wall, dripped into my oats or hay. It's most effective on the hiney of the Farm Manager's clean pants. If I sneeze, it creates a charming splatter effect that looks especially nice on the cookbook spines on that low shelf over there. Not to mention enhancement of the kitchen wallpaper. We buy baby cereal by the case, now, and in eight years, nobody at the grocery store has ever asked what the Farm Manager does with all of that baby cereal.

So far, the milk recipe sounds pretty normal, right? We capybaras have a persnickety digestive system, and we get belly aches for no detectable reason.

"Well, let's add some probiotic powder to his milk!" And so a spoonful of decidedly green powder adds to the murkiness. I saw the package once and it said "for pregnant mares" but that can't be right. "They need LOTS of Vitamin C!" And so a spoonful of white crystallized powder plops in there, too. That's not so bad, it still tastes sort of like milk.

If you are a picky eater and don't eat your vegetables and stay indoors too much, playing video games instead of poking around in the woods or investigating bugs or riding your bicycle or playing basketball, your bones might not grow as strong as they should. If you are especially klutzy and slip on the stairs you might even break your back.[31] If that was to happen, this is what else the Farm Manager might put into your milk: pain medication, calcium supplement, Vitamin D, magnesium and potassium capsules, and liquid glucosamine. The calcium supplement is a very nasty piece of work. The Farm Manager says it looks like the water that comes off curing concrete. The Bartender swears he has seen it at the bottom of utility vaults. I am glad I never see it before it is mixed into the milk. Why they bother with peppermint flavoring is one of the universe's big mysteries, but there is no way to disguise its presence in the milk. Still, I drink up all my milk twice a day, morning and night!

If I lived on a pretend farm, I could nap all morning. Unfortunately, the Farm Manager is completely incapable of running this place by herself, so I supervise the important tasks, like taste-testing the poultry feed. The Farm Manager is merely involved in opening gates and lifting heavy buckets. I chase the cats and wander around, dispersing ducks like waddling flotsam and jetsam in my wake. I sit in the dry corner of the barn and keep everybody out. I bump the Farm Manager's leg when Lula the hen gets her medicine. I beg to go into the Not For Dobby areas, like the big dome cage full of doves. I bite the hoses and up-end the treat dishes. I eat the lettuce as the Farm Manager distributes it to the ducks. I step in the clean water dishes and tip them over. Then the Farm Manager collects the eggs and it's naptime!

I'm very careful not to nap past 11:59 because of my noon corn. I push past the

---

31 I honestly don't know how I fractured my L7 vertebrae. It might have happened when I fractured my incisors.

WHO IS INVITED TO THE GARDEN PARTY?

❋ Norman the Goose, a noisy and bossy Flock Manager

❋ Cubicle, his shy goosy sidekick

❋ Shamrock, the shameless runner duck who follows Cubicle

❋ Boxcar and Boondock, two nondescript dumb Rouen drakes

❋ Emilio, third surly dumb Rouen drake

❋ Ping, Emilio's tiny white call girlfriend

❋ Vinny and Sal, the gangster runner drakes

❋ Tony, the Rouen mutt, rides shotgun with Vinny and Sal

❋ Carmen Miranda and Bev, a couple muscovy duck hussies

❋ Jello, an obnoxious old hen

❋ Adelita and Conchita, a pair of Welsummer hens

❋ Eartha, Windy, and Frieda, three portly golden laced Wyandotte hens

❋ Lula, the handicapped hen

❋ Princess Blur the Mille Fleur, Lula's puny caregiver

❋ NO CATS!

99

kitchen door at noon and the corn dispenser spits out an ear to me. Could be The Bartender, maybe the Farm Manager, but it's always one ear of corn. Never more. The service around here is very prompt except for twice a year when they suddenly trick me by changing lunchtime by an hour. Sometimes it's late, sometimes it's early, but it's always exactly an hour off. After a couple days of these shenanigans, I give in to the new world order and lunchtime stays regular for a long time after that.

One of the rules that I made up is that I must take my noon corn off the table to eat it. Long ago, everybody dropped it on the ground for me to eat. That's reasonable, you know, without hands it's easier for me to eat it on the ground. As royalty, my preference is for a more dignified presentation. We have a fancy pants Italian marble table on the deck right outside the kitchen. One day the Farm Manager put a piece of corn up there out of the way because she didn't want me to have it yet. She's such a fool. I stood up and took it down. From that day forward, I wouldn't eat corn from the ground; it has to be set on the table so I can take it down. True story.

I take five after wolfing down my corn. It's a good time for swimming or maybe a hot tub. Lately I have been baby-sitting a couple of hens. Lula is an old handicapped hen, and her caregiver, Princess Blur, is kind of casual about tending to her. In fact, she is downright useless. Handicapped animals have a way of getting "stuck" places, so that is the main thing to watch for. Sometimes I intervene when the wild crows and mallards crowd the food dish, but mostly I make sure there aren't any raccoons or hawks around. I'm a fine babysitter, except when I am napping.

One rule the Farm Manager takes seriously is the Princely Poop Pickup. She has a funky old masonry trowel and a dustpan, I think she's on the third one, but anyway she scoops everything up and takes it to my throne room. One day she added some *chicken poop to the dustpan*. Fortunately, I observed this blunder and head-butted her across the backyard! I might have even clicked at her! She must never contaminate my royal offerings with inferior deposits.

The best snack of the day is associated with the Garden Party. The ducks, chickens, and geese have a nice big pen, but they still like to explore my yard. Norman the goose starts announcing Garden Party at about 2:30 but the Farm Manager has been known to ignore his honking until 4:00, or even later! There's no turning back once she opens that gate.

The thug cat, Kitty Hawk is right there at the gate. As the hens scurry past him to the back yard, he bats each of their fluffy tails. The Farm Manager barks at him and then steers Hawk to the barn using his tail as a leash. She locks up both cats during the Garden Party so they don't escape.[32] Cats are 100% ungrateful. I'm sure they would eat me if I was any smaller. Fortunately, they are still excited about cat food, especially the canned "pâté." Canned cat food is vile stuff, concentrated essence of the very basest of life forms. I'd rather eat poop, and in fact, I do.

Once the cats are sequestered, the drakes all attack each other for a while and the rest of the flock settles into serious snacking, pecking, skritching, and sleeping. The local mallards fly down off the roof to join Mr. and Ms. Mallard in my swimming pool and then hop down to the snack dispensing area with the resident flock. The cracked corn and wild birdseed flows like wine, and then the Farm manager and I are called away on important business in the front yard. Unless I balk.

I have a lot of rules about the front yard, but the main one is that I don't have to go if I don't want to. Because I am as stubborn as a donkey. Conditions have to be perfect for the front yard excursion. The Farm Manager always comes with me, and she insists that I wear a harness. The weather must be good, no frozen ground, snow, any nastiness like that. There can't be any bad noises like leaf blowers, barking dogs, garbage trucks, little girls squealing their heads off. And there can't be scary smells. I don't go to the front yard, for instance, if it is windy. Coyotes skulk around in the stream corridor behind the houses across the street, and gusts of wind bring their B.O.[33] into my territory. No thank you, I will remain safely in my back yard, thank you very much.

---

32 Both our cats are adopted feral strays who can't be released back to their colonies because they tested positive for the FIV virus. They are thugs and like to fight, and that's what spreads FIV. Lock them up!
33 Body odor, duh.

Most days we simply parade out to the front, I diligently graze, and then come back home to the backyard. Ha ha ha, it's never that simple. There are three gates between the back yard and the front yard. Gate #3 and gate #4 are silly because one goes into the aviary and the other goes out. It seems like they cancel each other out, doesn't it? Fact is, it takes a lot of mistakes for me to accidentally get out of the back yard. Between Gate #2 and gate #3 is no-capybaras-land. There are shelves with dusty equipment, thousands of tools, a woodpile with thugs living under it, live traps in every size, from hamster to cat. (You shouldn't have to trap your own pets, but weird things happen around here all the time.) There are garbage cans full of feed and hay. In winter there is mud, in summer there are delicious weeds, and hanging on a hook is my grungy harness and leash.

While we traipse through here daily, I rarely have time to explore. It is a wondrous place with squirrels and bird nests. There are ropes to rub your morrillo on, all of those tools can be knocked over and marked. The grass that sprouts here is the tallest, sweetest grass in town. The mud in this area is exceptionally black and squishy. In fact, the best mud-rolling spot completely blocks the Farm Manager from going anywhere to do anything productive while she waits. What is she waiting for, anyway?

The Farm Manager has a few rules of her own. The most serious rule is the putting-on-of-the-harness. I have never been naked in the front yard. Hardly ever. We always stop at gate #2 before we venture out, and that's where the harness jumps onto me. This is, by design, the only place where I put on my harness. Ninety-nine percent of the time, we are going out to graze. That other teeny percent of time the leash goes on, too. That means a car ride, and car rides equal vet clinic visits. Thankfully, ferry rides never happen any more. We have gotten this far many times, standing patiently behind Gate #2, harness splayed out on the ground at my feet. And I deliberate. To harness or not to harness? Sometimes I step right in and nearly charge the gate. Most times I contemplate my navel while reluctantly holding up one foot, then another as the Farm Manager scampers from one side to the other, clicking the buckle shut over my shoulders. This always makes the gate open, and then we wander out to the front yard. That "we" is the Farm Manager's rule. She always goes with me to the front yard.[34] She tells me it's so I don't get lonely, but I know it's really so I don't open a gate, walk down to the bus stop, and go the grocery store to buy corn.

You don't know what happens next because the part about my tricks is in the next chapter. (Unless you are a cheater who skips ahead.) This is when we do them, starting with the super-lame trick I just told you about, Putting on the Harness. It can be trickier than you can possibly imagine. My favorite part of doing tricks is taking the biggest bites of reward corn that I can, super fast, before she pulls the corn away. I also like to take bites really close to the corn handle, you know, that's the part the Farm Manager hangs onto while I scarf down as much as I can. I can make her drop that sucker if I take a fast bite near the handle! Anyway, tricks are exclusively a Front Yard game.

Sometimes it seems like we have a dozen different front yards. When you hear people talking about the "dead of winter," they are talking about my poor front yard. The grass seems to get sucked down into the ground, the tiny tips barely showing above the standing water. It is so soggy that mud happens wherever we walk, so we try to keep to narrow trails. The water level rises and falls with each rainfall event, but you know the groundwater is fully recharged when the water table has been an inch above the lawn for a month. The neighborhood robins gave up on worms here a long time ago. There is a flock of a dozen of them munching away three houses down, but our worms all have scuba gear on, very unpalatable to robins. I don't eat worms, but looking around, there is precious little edible greenery. Still not tempted to sample worms. Thank goodness for the bamboo hedge!

In the spring, the front yard insults me by favoring the nasty plants I shouldn't eat: the horsetail (*Equisetum* species) and buttercups (*Ranunculus* species). We even have nightshade (*Solanum* species) creeping over the north fence. And then there are the rhododendrons, azaleas, and lily-of-the-valley shrub but they are

---

34 Seriously, she thinks if I get outside the fence, someone will assume I'm an alien species and shoot me. She has deluded herself into thinking that everyone knows that extraterrestrials don't wear harnesses, and therefore, with a harness on, I am less likely to become target practice for somebody's drunken redneck uncle.

all fenced off. The Farm Manager collects as much horsetail as she can, but I don't think she's eating it so she should be okay. She grazes funny. She picks it and puts it in a bucket, just like when she picks my bamboo, except it goes away instead of into the kitchen.

Fortunately, once the daylight hours start to lengthen, the grass goes a little bit crazy. There is little clumpy grass, bigger regular grass, gigantic big honking grass twice as tall as me, and poky grass called sedge that likes the soggy places. I like to give it a haircut! We have dandelions, too! They are probably my favorite. I think I should be able to invite my capybara friends over for a Group Graze. Maybe for the whole summer.

Some of the other good things to eat are the blackberry that grows like a magic beanstalk. I don't mind the thorns. The wild roses are thorny, too, but they aren't as tasty as the fancy roses in the back yard. (What happened to those, anyway? There used to be a lot more of them!). Blueberries are tasty, too. The plants, I mean, I bite off big branches. Most of those have cages around them, now.

The grass is literally greener on the other side of the fence, though. I can see it through the chain link fabric. Nobody grazes there except for ducks because it is a huge wetland, but I can see the watercress and duckweed in the big pond. In springtime there are millions of ducklings there. If I went over there, I would eat all of the duckweed in one afternoon: enough to feed them all until they grew up. That's cool, the ducklings need their breakfast, but I don't understand why I can't graze there during no-ducklings season. The Farm Manager mutters about how I would never come home if I got over there, and she's right. I could fill out a change of address form at the post office and find a new old lady to feed me corn and dandelions one-at-a-time. She might even tuck me in at night, so what's the problem with that?

This is kind of embarrassing, but even though I have no qualms about pooping in The Farm Manager's kitchen, I will not poop in the front yard. In eight years, I have never left a deposit out there. Oh, I do some marking with urine, sure, and I rub my morrillo on everything. But there is no pooping in the front yard.

Ever. When I was tiny, the front yard was only partially fenced. I wasn't allowed out there because I could walk right underneath the fences. The Farm Manager eventually had the fence fixed and gates put on. There is even wire fence inside the bamboo hedge, but you can't see it. Anyway, before the fence was done, coyotes pooped in the yard! The front yard is a dead end, though: there's no way to get out if they come in and get cornered. They haven't pooped out there in years, but they still hang out across the street. I can smell their stinky butts from here, and when the wind blows, it is bone-chilling! I am a prey animal, and it's not too smart to advertise my presence, better to be subtle. So the no-poop rule is serious out in the front yard. That means that every once in a while we need to go to the back yard in a hurry, and I have to stand around, legs crossed, until we get there.

One of the Farm Manager's front yard rules is that I have to go back when it gets dark. This is completely arbitrary, of course. Wild capybaras prefer to graze dusk and dawn. I long ago saw the folly of the dawn part of that plan. Dusk though, that is the best time to graze. Did you know that grass is more nutritious at the end of the day? It gathers up nutrients during daylight hours and doesn't do much with them until the sun goes down. That's the best time for me to bite the heads off of the grass. But, oh no, "Not For Dobby!" I always have to return to the back yard before it gets dark. That's not quite true, though. There have been some warm summer evenings when the Farm Manager lets me linger. Sometimes, if I beg really hard, ask nicely, she'll even let me go back out to the front yard a second time, at dusk. Same rules though, harness goes back on, Farm Manager has to come, too.

I am responsible for most of the fun rules, and they happen to revolve around my bedtime milk. Morning milk is beyond my control, but The Bartender is quite consistent about the timing and even the measurement of the ingredients. Extremely predictable. All heck breaks loose at bedtime, though. The Farm Manager thinks it's funny to change milk time according to her own whims. When visitors show up around bedtime and the frenetic kitchen activity is focused around equipment she never uses for my milk, I know I am doomed. Same thing if the front door slams, a car drives away, and the house echoes like an abandoned quarry. There is only one appropriate Dobby-response to abandonment at milk time.

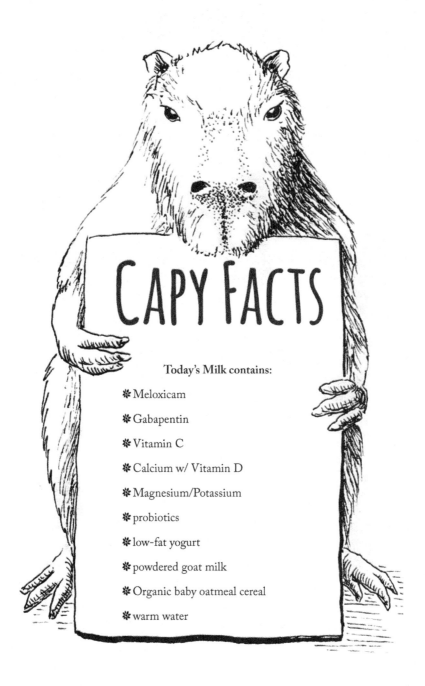

CAPY FACTS

Today's Milk contains:

❋ Meloxicam

❋ Gabapentin

❋ Vitamin C

❋ Calcium w/ Vitamin D

❋ Magnesium/Potassium

❋ probiotics

❋ low-fat yogurt

❋ powdered goat milk

❋ Organic baby oatmeal cereal

❋ warm water

The kitchen door, where I watch the squirrels abscond with my used corn cobs.

Usually, though, the milk happens like clockwork around going-dark time. Well, not in summer, because that's 10:00! And not in winter because 4:30 is way too early for anybody to go to bed. Might as well hibernate. So when the sun starts setting, and the garden party is over and the hens are roosting, I start waiting for my milk. I go in and out the kitchen door a kajillion times. I jingle the bells that hang on the doorknob. I haul hay and bird seed off the shelves and toss toys around. Might poop in the kitchen. Then I go sit outside the door where I can listen and watch for milk-time activities through the transparent kitchen door. If nothing happens, I go in and out the door, re-jingling the bells. The Farm

Manager can hear those from far away, and she'll eventually give up and make my milk. What could possibly be more important than making my milk?

I can hear the Farm Manager's footsteps on the stairs: I think the Dobby refrigerator is downstairs. She fetches a head of romaine lettuce and an ear of corn. Next, the upstairs refrigerator opens and closes, a cupboard door slams shut. Now most of the activity is at the kitchen sink. Jars and bottles clunk onto the counter. My milk is magic and contains many secret ingredients, but I am a vegetarian so I am not concerned about newt eyeballs, frog toes or anything like that.

The waiting is painful, but near the end, I can hear the lid of the goat milk canister popping off and that's when I finally come back into the kitchen for the final waiting. This is my favorite routine, because I made the whole thing up! When the Farm Manager enters my area with the milk bowl, I sneeze! It's a big sneeze, and my fur pouffs up and my whole body shakes, like a dog drying his fur! Sometimes I sneeze a couple times. Then I turn a circle the milk way, clockwise. We're almost ready to take the milk outside to my pen, but I have one more trick: I stand up for the lettuce! Now the Milk Ceremony is complete, and the Milk Parade can proceed out to my pen. My potato bowl and maybe some bamboo magically appears while I have my face in my milk bowl. You can go now, g'nite.

THE THIRD TIME I ALMOST DIED

You might think I'm joking about these dramatic brushes with death, but the third time was a close one. I wrote this story about a week after a disastrous veterinary procedure. This clinic had recently moved into a brand new facility with a big parking lot and no dog food stores next door. The veterinarian had excellent credentials. "Everything looked good on paper," or in this case, on the website, but I almost died getting a blood draw, dental exam, and three radiographs. So, here is my third near-death experience.

The Farm Manager peels back the corn husks as I impatiently dance and spin in the front yard. A few weeks ago I could bite straight through the husk like it was limp lettuce or a graham cracker. I could take big bites out of the corn like humans do, except my sharp incisors cut straight through the cob, too. One week ago I couldn't bite through grass. I could only nibble at husked corn. The week before that I couldn't bite . . . anything at all. I had never fully appreciated my rodenthood, but having teeth that automatically grow back is a blessing and a joy. We capybaras are truly amazing, and once again I, Prince Dobalob, sometimes known simply as Sir Dobby, am demonstrating our wonderfulness.

I am certain my faithful followers are wondering what happened to my front teeth, but to be perfectly honest, I am wondering that very same thing. You see, I was unconscious when it happened. The Farm Manager and The Bartender were close by, but there was a solid wall between us. I went behind the wall with two perfect front teeth, and emerged from behind the wall with two fractured front teeth, my upper incisors, my pride and joy, broken but still hanging on. Where is that UNDO button when you need it? And why was I unconscious?

I am a slender capy, always have been, but I have gradually lost weight—8 pounds—over the last two years. My World Famous Brother, Caplin, had been gradually losing weight before his sudden death in 2010. The Farm Manager decided it was time for a checkup. Dr. F, my regular veterinarian was unavailable, so we decided to break in a new one. The Farm Manager interviewed a few exotic animal clinics and selected one. The clinic was a beautiful new facility and the veterinarian was knowledgeable and confident. The Farm Manager made an appointment, and I cooperated by getting into my harness, hopping into the car, and we made it to our appointment early! For a wild animal, I am a pretty good boy. Sometimes.

It was a quick car ride and I barely had time to get sick! The parking lot was huge. I stayed in the car with the Farm Manager while The Bartender popped inside to say hello. They recommended bringing me in through a side door to the clinic, so the Farm Manager led me down a walkway to the secret paparazzi-free back entrance. The door slammed shut behind us and we were in a clean but featureless chamber with cold concrete floors. That smelled like bobcat.

"Nonsense," the vet tech said. "We cleaned thoroughly since the bobcat was here yesterday. Plus, he was never out of his carrier."

The Farm Manager's eyes opened wide, blinking.

It is always easier for the vet to work on a sedated wild animal than an angry, awake one. Instead of giving me one simple surprise injection like Dr. F does, they stuck me in the back a couple times with expensive butterfly needles.[35] I ran around like a picked bull, angrier and angrier after each attempt. Finally, I was properly stuck and then they had to chase me down to inject the sedative. The Farm Manager looked on in shock.

While the tranquilizer worked its fuzzy magic, the plan was discussed by the humans, as if capybara input was moot. I would provide a blood sample, they would take three radiographs (stabbing me again, but with painless X-rays), and do a dental exam. Rodents and Lagomorphs[36] are notorious for dental problems, so if we are losing weight, naughty teeth are likely suspects. While we were waiting for the sedative to knock me flat, the Farm Manager asked me to touch my nose to a target so that everyone could have a look at my big beautiful incisors! I would have brushed my teeth if I had known the scrutiny they would receive, but whatever. They are still impressive. And at that time, they were perfectly intact.

When I was almost too groggy to walk, the Farm Manager coaxed me across the hall, through a door, and then they took her from me. She protested, of course, but Clinic Policy, yada yada yada, I forget the rest. They returned her to me an hour and a half later, apologizing for the fractured teeth (showing her the radiographs) but offering no explanation as to how it had happened. And I could go home now. The good news was that, other than the spontaneously fractured upper incisors, my teeth were in great shape, possibly a wee bit of bone loss in the jaw to watch. My blood work was normal, as far as they know (and they don't know beans) except for the thyroid levels, but what are normal thyroid levels in a capybara? I have cataracts, but I have had those for 5 years. Oh, and I have dandruff. Kind of embarrassing, will have to get rid of the black turtleneck sweaters.

---

35 A butterfly needle is a pricey fancy pants needle the vet sticks into a vein. It has a tube attached so you can put medicine in or take blood out. Ouch! Hurts like a regular needle!
36 Such a fancy word for rabbits!

So off I went, drunk as a skunk, with my little souvenir bag of Critical Care[37]—two gigantic bags, actually—and four wobbly legs. I don't remember going out to the car. I don't remember the drive home. I don't remember getting out of the car. I do remember that even now, broken and beaten, I was not allowed to go in through the front door. No, they dragged me around to the service entrance, you know, the door the Farm Manager uses, and locked me in. Not really, but they barricaded me onto the deck so I wouldn't stumble down the stairs, you know, might break my front teeth or something. But I got to sleep inside, or so they tell me, because I really don't remember anything that happened on those two days. The exam was on a Tuesday, but I snoozed through Wednesday, and didn't really start to recover from the anesthesia until Thursday. By Friday, I could almost walk a straight line. But I still couldn't eat.

---

37   Oxbow Critical Care® is a food supplement designed to meet the nutritional needs of rabbits and guinea pigs after surgery or whenever it is absolutely essential to ensure that they are eating properly. Generally, it is fed via syringe (just like corn syrup), only it's chunky and gritty because it is full of ground up hay.

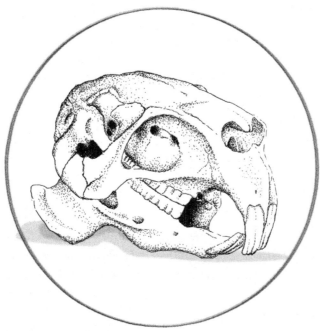

I'm magnificent, inside and out!

Can you imagine getting smacked in the face so hard that your two upper incisors (those big front ones) fracture, but not enough that they fall out? They are kind of dangling there, useless, and your mouth is sore. I even had cuts in my mouth that the Farm Manager put ointment on for a few days. Nobody knew when my teeth would fall out, but we thought it might take a week, maybe two, for them to grow out to where they would break off. We heard from other capybara owners that they usually grow completely back in two weeks. The Farm Manager and The Bartender started talking optimistically about their trip to Florida on Saturday, but nobody started packing. And then my two front teeth fell out on Thursday afternoon.[38]

---

38 See the upper incisors (big front teeth) on the skull drawing? The gum tissue covers the bone and extends a bit past the top of the tooth, just like yours. Mine are different because the bone extends behind and around the teeth for support. Behind the incisors and over the bone, there is tissue that glues it all together. My upper incisors broke off way up at the top, right about where the teeth emerge from the skull. When my incisors fell out, it exposed the bloody tissue underneath. It was gruesome. (By the way, if you follow the curve of the upper and lower incisors back to where the molars are, that's about where the "tooth bud" is, where my constantly growing teeth are formed. They are *big teeth*, much bigger than you can see from outside my mouth.)

When I first arrived home from the veterinary clinic that Tuesday, I didn't walk around too much. I was embarrassed about the stumbling, and frankly, I didn't feel so hot. On Tuesday night, I had pushed my way through the barricade at the top of the stars to demonstrate that I could carefully catapult myself down them without mishap. The Farm Manager reluctantly removed both barricades. On Wednesday, it became clear that I had no intention of eating anything ever again. I was walking better, but I still wasn't sober, and I was too scared to go to the front yard. I was still interested in my milk, which, by the way, picked up some strange gritty flavors. The only grass I could eat was the tenderest slender blades. No long or coarse grasses, no potatoes, no hay, no corn, no matter how they sliced it.

The Farm Manager suddenly noticed that although the vet had thoughtfully sent her home with Critical Care,® the vet had NOT sent her home with pain medication, the most obvious and most dire need after being smacked in the mouth with an anvil. She sent The Bartender back to the vet for pain meds, enough to bankrupt us but allow me to survive through to their Going-to-Florida-on-Saturday abandonment plan. Obviously, I would veto any staff vacations if I was still in pain on Friday.

Even with the newly acquired pain meds, on Thursday I stopped walking around. I sat in one place for a while, then another, quivering my lips and clenching my teeth. The Farm Manager came over to chat and noticed my bloody tooth on the ground. I had vetoed the Florida vacation.

Now she knew why the vet had sent me home with two huge packages of guinea pig food supplement. Critical Care® is an amazing mixture of hay, probiotics, vitamins, and minerals. When mixed with water, it turns into an aromatic sludge that a few guinea pigs eat readily, the rest not so much. For the reluctant ones, the technique is to roll your guinea pig into a towel "burrito," hold them firmly, insert the filled syringe into the side of their mouth, in the gap between the incisors and molars (their little skull looks a lot like mine!) and squirt a conservative amount into their mouth. Readers of this book now know more about capybaras than this veterinarian. The vet had supplied four gargantuan syringes. What do you think? Will The Prince take Critical Care® through a syringe?[39]

---

39 Of course not, silly.

For the next couple of weeks, the Farm Manager sliced all my food into bite-sized morsels and slipped them into my mouth through the convenient gap between my incisors and my molars. I passed the days eating soft clipped grass, lettuce, and crunchy milk. I couldn't pick up anything with my mouth, and though my molars were fine, chewing with my strange new (lack of) dentition made my jaw sore, and after a few hand-fed bites, I yawed and refused any more. The Farm Manager had found the other tooth and I was relieved to have the no-longer-wiggly relics displayed on her desk instead of tormenting my poor beat-up mouth. I suffered through another day without pain meds before the Farm Manager relented and sent The Bartender out for more.

Let's talk about teeth again. Take another look at the capybara bonehead drawing. You already know about the big gap between my Bucky Beavers (upper incisors) and my molars. That's because capybaras have no canine teeth. Let that sink in. Duh, right? Anyway, when my teeth grew back, the back side of my incisors gradually reattached to the tissue over my palate. It took more than two weeks for my incisors to grow as far as the end of the palate, and all that time my mouth was too sore to bite things. You already know that my rodent teeth grow all the time, even the molars, and if you ate tough muddy grass, you would want your teeth to keep growing, too. The grit wears them down as fast as they grow. When I bite grass, my teeth work like scissors, cutting and sharpening with each bite, because the top surface is hard enamel, and the inner surface is a little softer. That edge is like a razor blade. (I'm saying that with an evil grin.) That's why the incisors had to grow well beyond that palate edge before they could meet up with the lower incisors to start the sharpening process. So that I could graze again.

Ironically, I lost four pounds while recovering from my why-am-I-losing-weight exam. Almost four weeks later, my poop volume was nearly normal, and my weight stabilized. Another week of sharpening my teeth on grass, and I was back to biting corn cobs. Eventually I gained my four pounds back, but I still haven't gained back the eight I lost before that. I have other problems, now, but the teeth are back to normal. Hurray for rodent teeth that grow 1/8th inch a day!

Chapter Five

WHAT ARE WE TALKING ABOUT?

I understand English, so watch what you say! Dogs certainly understand a lot of words, and some cats even admit to knowing some. Sure, a bunch of it is contextual, and I can tell a lot by the tone of your voice, but I have an extensive vocabulary, for a rodent.

My favorite words are food words:

- ❉ Apple
- ❉ Bamboo
- ❉ Banana Chip
- ❉ Corn
- ❉ Dandelion
- ❉ Grass
- ❉ Lettuce
- ❉ Milk
- ❉ Pear
- ❉ Potato
- ❉ Raisin

I also know some names:

- ❉ Dick (you might know him as The Bartender)
- ❉ Dobby (I know my own name, too!)

But not the Farm Manager. She doesn't have a name.

I even made up my own name for The Bartender! When I want milk, I smack my lips, kind of like a goldfish. One time the Farm Manager and I were in the front yard. A car drove into the driveway, on the far side of the bamboo hedge, where I couldn't see it. I was a little scared when I heard the car door open and close, but the Farm Manager said, "It's Dick." I looked at her and did my milk mouth thing. She looked at me, puzzled, and repeated "It's Dick, Dobby." I smacked my lips again. Then she got it! The Bartender prepares my milk in the morning, so I call him "Milk!" I was telling her that I knew it was Dick getting out of the car.

I know the difference between a Visitor and a Neighbor. Visitors expect me to do some tricks, do a little Doofus Dance. When the Farm Manager announces that a visitor is coming, I know to expect to see strangers in the kitchen gawking at me. We don't care about neighbors. They make strange and sudden off-site noises that I can ignore. They don't turn into visitors very often, but it does happen.

I know my co-pets, too:

- ❋ Chickens
- ❋ Ducks
- ❋ Kitties
- ❋ Norman (the goose and flock manager)
- ❋ Princess (why is this hen always in the backyard?)
- ❋ Rabbit
- ❋ Squirrels (wild ones are all over the place)

Of course, there are my tricks, and I promise you we will be getting to those:

- ❋ Give Farm Manager a kiss
- ❋ Lie down
- ❋ Lie down and roll over
- ❋ Ring around the Rosie (walk all the way around the Farm Manager)
- ❋ Sit
- ❋ Sneeze (includes a shake)

* Stand up
* Touch your nose (to the target)
* Turn around the Corn Way (counter-clockwise)
* Turn around the Milk Way (clockwise)
* Wave bye-bye

I know some random body parts:

* Ears
* Eyeball
* Feet
* Morrillo
* Nose
* Tail (ha ha, joking. I don't have a tail!)

One time when I went to the vet for an eye boo-boo, my regular vet, Dr. F wasn't there. Dr. M was nervous about looking in my big old eye, but the Farm Manager explained to me that the vet was going to look at my eyeball. I know what eyeball means, so I wasn't at all surprised when she leaned over, put drops in, and looked in there with a bright light. When the Farm Manager had to put medicine in there, she would talk to me about it first so I would know we were doing the eyeball goop again. I'm pretty good about letting people stick things into my eye.

I understand the relationship of these words to places:

* Chicken time (the aviary)
* Kitchen
* Front yard
* Hot tub

I also understand these phrases:

* Go swimming

I have gone swimming on command, but it is dependent upon ambient air and water temperatures. If it is a nice day, I'll do a little Doofus Dance, hop up the steps, check for alligators, taste the water, of course, and then dive right in! Sometimes I jump up onto the steps without diving in, just to prove that I know what the conversation is about, then I turn around and come back down.

❊ Come here

Understanding "come here" and doing it are not related. Sometimes I am busy, sometimes I disapprove of the weather, other times I simply don't see the point.

❊ Not for Dobby

"Not For Dobby" was inspired by a book called *Wesley the Owl*. In that book, a woman raises an owl, but the owl is in charge of everything. Wesley is much more demanding than I am, so he had the entire house to fly around in, and that is very dangerous. Anyway, the book explains how the woman addressed the problem of disciplining her tame wild animal. The problem is that if you tell me, or any other wild animal *"no!"* you could get bit. I am royalty, so telling me to stop doing something makes no sense, it only makes me angry.[40] Wesley's owner used the phrase "Not For Owls!" to let Wesley know that he was getting into something potentially dangerous. Using his name caught his attention and seemed to diffuse the anger. It works for me, too. I like hearing my name, and I don't want to do anything that might hurt me, so I pay attention when she says "Not For Dobby!" It's not something I hear very often, so I take it pretty seriously when I hear it.

❊ Good boy
❊ *Very* good boy

Good boy is something I'm confused about, because the Farm Manager often uses this phrase to mean "poop." The funny thing is that she only calls my poop "good boy" when it's outside! If it's inside she doesn't say anything worth repeating. And then when she says "Very good boy" she's talking about me. It's confusing, but I like the way she says it and I often get pouffy, if I'm not already.

---

40   Most animal trainers recognize that positive reinforcement achieves better long-term results than negative reinforcement, especially for non-domestic (wild) animals.

❃ Chicken time

Chicken time happens every morning when we go out to feed the chickens. I like to help the chickens and ducks eat their lettuce. It's also important for me to mark any tools that the Farm Manager uses out there, especially rakes and shovels. I inspect the cats and make certain they are in the barn where they're supposed to be, not wandering around the aviary. Lately we keep getting used chickens, and they are scared of me at first. I try to make them feel at home by doing some Doofus Dancing, sniffing their butts, tasting their food to make sure it's okay, stuff like that. When new hens arrive, the Farm Manager herds them into a pen that I usually have access to. She shuts the gate to keep everybody from harassing them. I need to personally inspect all new hens, so I spend a lot of time begging to get in there, or maybe sneaking in. That leads us to the phrase:

❃ Don't Let the Chickens* Out!

*or ducks or kitties

Every time the Farm Manager opens a gate, all the hens crowd around and try to escape. Sometimes this is okay, like at garden party time in the afternoon when they are all going to come out anyway. Of course, it's never okay for the cats to come out because they are thugs. Anyway, it takes me a long time to do anything because I am a capybara and our standard mode is slow motion. When she says, "don't let the chickens out" I move ever so slightly faster and push the chickens out of the way with my big snout. It's fun to watch them scamper. When she says, "don't let the kitties out" those rascals are usually already trying to push past me so they're kind of under my legs and I barge on through and swish them back in with me.

❃ Excuse me

Capybaras are wild animals, and tame pet capybaras are much less wary than the wild ones, but you really don't want to sneak up on me. The problem is that I always seem to be standing around blocking traffic. It's by design. If you approach and try to squeeze past me, I will interpret that move as aggression. I might even snap at you. So, if you find yourself in a narrow corridor with a capybara, simply say "excuse me!" and they will let you pass. It's like when humans are on a busy bus, and the same thing happens. If you brush past someone on the way out the door "excuse me" expresses a request to enter their personal space, while silently brushing past someone implies that you are a pickpocket. None of us tolerate an invasion of personal space gracefully, but I have bigger incisors than you do.

❋ Pretty soon

This doesn't seem to mean anything, but I put it on the list anyway, because the Farm Manager says this all the time. For one thing, she almost always wanders away after she says it. Plus, no matter what she was talking about, it's guaranteed not to happen very soon. For instance, "Corn pretty soon" means I can forget about corn for a while, and she'll probably go away. I think this one is related to "I'll be right back" which seems to be meaningless, but also announces a departure. Why say anything at all? I don't get it.

❋ Careful!

You might think that capybaras are athletic and nimble and maybe some are. I am a prime candidate for the Klutzy Capybara Club. Have you noticed how our front legs are shorter than our back legs? *Not* a good design for going downstairs, though I can scramble on up, no problem. The Farm Manager always says "Careful!" when we're going up and down stairs, though I am very cautious so she's being a bit overcautious.

Right now, the kitchen deck is slick as snot. All of the corn mess, apple juice and cores, and other unsavory deposits out there are bad enough. In fall, though, we have buckets of rain, and it's still warm enough to cook up a gelatinous skim coat of slime. It's as treacherous for humans in skid-proof boots as it is for capybaras with all-natural Vibram© soles. Someone is going to land on their butt out there, and that's why she keeps saying "Careful!"

Gates. I have a love-hate relationship with gates. Some open in, some open out, and some seem to change back and forth. If it was up to me, I would get rid of all of them. They swing open very close to my little tootsies. In fact, gates are why I know how fast foot booboos heal! "Careful!"

I like to mark things with my morrillo. Tools are my favorite things to mark. I want to mark that shovel, and your rake! What's that, a machete? "Careful!"

I like to barge in on the Farm Manager when she is in her greenhouse, the little house in the front yard where it doesn't rain. There are plants to eat, plastic pots to mash and toss, buckets of gross green water, sticks and tools at eye level. "Careful!"

My hot tub is cleverly disguised as a cheap plastic wading pool. It's only hot when the Farm Manager fills it from the hose connected to the water heater, and that water comes out as hot as McDonald's coffee! Of course, I want to be as close as possible to the stream of steamy hot water. "Careful!"

Sometimes I go away somewhere, clip a leash to that harness, go through forbidden Gate #1 and down the rickety stairs, "Careful!" When I get into the car, I scrabble up a ramp to the back seat, "Careful!"

What a worry wart!

SAY WHAT?

As you can see, the English language has limited utility. Because the Farm Manager and I spend so much time together, I have helped her out by teaching her capybara language.

The first capybara word I taught her was "come here." You tilt your head to the side and quickly point up with your chin. She picked right up on that one. It was quite a while before I learned the English for it. I suspect that if she spoke better Portuguese life would be simpler, but she learned a little bit and then went right back to English. I continue to lobby for Portuguese.

Hmmm. When I think about it, "come here" is the only word she has learned in capybara. Her potential is very limited if that is her crowning achievement. I think we'll gloss over that fact and I'll tell you the other capybara language that I've tried to teach her. Like I told her my name for Dick (The Bartender) but she persists in using his English name.

The most fun way to say I'm happy is Doofus Dancing. I guarantee you the Farm Manager will never learn that. I stand behind her and dance when she can't see me. Sometimes I follow her and dance. When she turns around and sees the dancing I stop. I like to tease her and it makes The Bartender laugh when he catches me in the act. Second, capybaras have our spectacular piloerection[41] display. She would look brilliant if she could do it, but she refuses to even try that one. And finally, our other happy tell is the ear wiggle. We wiggle our ears exactly the way hippopotamuses do! We both loll around all day in water, so maybe there is some anatomical basis for this ear wiggling style. On the other hand, it has recently come to my attention that giraffes wiggle their ears, too. Sort of dashes that theory, doesn't it? We've got no tail to wag, so the ear wiggle is an extremely positive sign, if you are concerned about the disposition of your capybara. She claims to be working on that one but I'm pretty sure she has no tail.

Herd animals, like cows, communicate constantly, and so do we. We chitter[42] like a Geiger counter, guinea pig, or a raccoon. It is whisper quiet, not as strident as your wheeking guinea pig. Baby capybaras chitter, too, but they also make a high-pitched capybara version of the wheek. Grown-up royal capybaras that are spoiled and still drink milk make those wheeky noises as they follow the Farm Manager or The Bartender to their pen at milk time. If I am in the kitchen when the Farm Manager walks through, I chitter a greeting to her. When I am in the front yard I chitter occasionally to let her know I am near. I expect a proper answer but she persists in English.

I have subtle communications, too. When I want milk I move my lips like a goldfish but I do that to ask for other things, too, like banana chips or more corn.

---

41   Check out page 27 in your copy of *Capyboppy*!
42   It's between a trill and purr.

Lately I have been smacking my lips in an exaggerated way, and that means, "I want dandelions, now!" I also have a very low single tsk- almost a click- that I do when I approve of something. I tsk when I agree to let the Farm Manager put my harness on after I have been horsing around and wasting her time. It's the tsk of approval. I also make a very deep thrum, like the low rumble that elephant stomachs make. Humans can barely hear it. We haven't told them what it means, though, big secret! One time I talked, made kind of a growly noise.[43] We're not telling what that means, either.[44] My newest vocalization is the "I love my chickens" conversation I have when I share my birdseed with the hens. It is a happy noise and comes with a complimentary pouffy fur display.

I bray like a donkey![45] I love the Farm Manager so much that sometimes when I see her in the morning I bray. Sometimes, out of the blue, she goes away for a couple days. I have learned to accept that the Farm Manager comes back, but I bray when she returns home. I have brayed for my human sister, and once I even brayed for The Bartender, which embarrassed both of us, so I probably won't do that again. Sheesh.

Wait, there's more! I bark, too! My bark[46] is quiet, more of a huff, really. I doubt the neighbors can even hear it. (They sure can hear me smacking a bucket around at midnight, though!) I bark once, maybe a few times, but usually they are isolated huffs, like a dog lacking confidence. Mostly, I bark when I hear or smell something I can't see. I bark at the wind if it brings coyote cooties into my territory. A car door slamming next door can do it, too. Lawn mowers and chainsaws and other manly noises don't bother me. What I don't bark at is noises that sound like a small animal being tortured, like those little girls next door and their incessant squealing. Smart prey animals silence themselves when predators are nearby. Noisy prey animals get eaten first.

Well, actually, that's not quite true for me. I bark at possums and raccoons, but I have a very secure night pen. Nothing is getting in there, except maybe a rat.

---

43 It's on YouTube! *Talk to me, Dobby* https://youtu.be/P2hsHwxKQLY
44 It was a meaningless campaign promise.
45 Stop snickering!
46 Hear me bark on YouTube! *Barking at a Cat* https://youtu.be/kLLrjjwmzIs

(They eat my leftovers.) That means I am extremely confident that I am safe at night. We have owls and stray cats and all sorts of crazy interlopers that don't concern me, but the possums and raccoons are scary. I bark and dare them to eat me and still feel safe.

Lest everyone think I'm a pushover, my aggressive tendencies are no joke. I've already told you about how I head-butted the Farm Manager for a poop cleanup error. I also head-butted both the Farm Manager and The Bartender when they tried to put my harness on at the cabin. It's a little more complicated than that, and I was only play-butting that time. In a serious head-butt situation, I approach rapidly, with my mouth open, teeth bared. It's kind of a pre-bite situation. In the wild, mature male capybaras stand up and fight, biting heads and shoulders. Our skin is like leather, though, so it is hard for us to really damage each other. Human skin isn't nearly as tough. I bit my human sister on the finger when she tried to be the Farm Manager, and she had to get stitches. I felt bad about it afterward, and the following summer I forgave her. I very gently licked her arm and she knew were friends again.

By far the most aggressive memo I have released is the Stomp-&-Click. This is not something you want to see up close. My early warning system is self-explanatory, so there's no reason to let things escalate. I suppose most of you have heard squirrels chatter. It's a noise they make with their teeth. Guinea pigs make a similar noise. It's a rodent thing. Now, imagine a squirrel on steroids chattering. My skull is a resonating chamber, so it's quite loud. They can barely hear me bark, but the neighbors might be able to hear my clicking. It's very impressive.

When do I click? Well, first there's that warning click. I don't like snow, so I have been known to click at snowflakes.[47] I realize how silly that sounds, but it's kind of like stubbing your toe: bad words come out automatically. Snow is really annoying and I can't keep my opinion about that a secret. I also click at the plushies in the kitchen, also a waste of time, but who is it, exactly, who lines them up every morning so they're all staring at me? I used to share my kitchen space with a guinea pig named Ziggy. He used to stare at me, too. What would

---

47   Hear me click at snowflakes on YouTube! *I Don't Like Snow* https://youtu.be/JvdbZaXNXOM

you do? There's always a parakeet in the kitchen. Don't they ever shut up? I click at you, Spitfire the Budgie! Sometimes humans are a bit slow at doling out the dandelions. You do that, you're going to get clicked at! Got a piece of corn stuck in my teeth. "Dammit." That's all warning clicking, nice and quiet, subdued, but I'm unmistakably annoyed.

It's the other clicking you need to know about. When I am furious, there's no mistaking it. I click at people who visit too long and are presumptuous about their standing.[48] When I stomp and spin around while I'm clicking, attack is imminent. Okay, sometimes I stomp and click at the plushies, but it's usually about something serious, such as unauthorized use of my washer or dryer. I stomp and click at cat blankets being washed. I stomp and click at the possum and raccoon in the back yard at night. I even stomp and click at the Farm Manager, who is part capybara, after all. She should know better, but I do have to straighten her out once in a while.

FUN AND GAMES: REVISITING MY GOALS

One day as she was struggling at the kitchen door to get her mud boots off, I saw my chance and pushed past the Farm Manager into the house. I immediately saw that the Dobby-Gate was open so I walked on into the kitchen. I could hear her saying bad words to her boots, now, but I saw that the door to the stairway was open, too, so I kept going. I love that feeling of carpet on my toes and started to turn a lazy circle on the landing beyond the doorway.

"No! Dobby, no!" said the Farm Manager, skidding through the kitchen in her stocking feet. I escaped up the stairs into the bedroom, where I used to sleep when I was a baby. My favorite stuff is up there, like the Forbidden Closet, and my favorite under-the-desk lounging area. But I didn't get that far. I saw a most wondrous thing in my old sleeping corner: a brand new white rabbit rug! Even from far away I could tell it wasn't as nice (smelly) as my old one, but still it was such a beautiful sight that I stopped right there, frozen in a classic capybara pose, like a life-sized plastic figurine.

---

48   Hear me click at Melanie on YouTube! *Dobby Throws a Tantrum* https://youtu.be/DmYt2RPhCyA

Before I knew what was happening she barged in behind me and pushed me out of the bedroom back into the hall. I started down the stairs this time but I started to get mad until I saw—ha ha ha!—that my feet were making muddy footprints like a cartoon! So funny! But even though I kept trying to on the way out, she wouldn't let me poop or pee or even mark the rugs, so the excursion was somewhat of a failure from that standpoint.[49] As a reconnaissance run, though, it was quite satisfactory. A little more practice, more confidence and determination, and I'll be rip snorting back up there in no time.

OF COURSE, I CAN DO TRICKS

Yes, in fact, more than two! The Farm Manager doesn't understand everything I say or do, but I am very proud that she has learned so many of my tricks. When we get into a sticky situation, it is helpful that we have established two-way communication. My confidence grows as we understand each other and the more she learns, the more comfortable I am.

One of the first tricks we perfected was the Putting-On-Of-The-Harness. I was minuscule and not too savvy when the Farm Manager started putting me in straitjackets. First it was kind of a joke, "See how cute you look in a cat harness?" It wasn't cute at all and I felt like Scarlett O'Hara in that *Gone with the Wind* scene where Mammy was cinching her into that corset. I could barely move in that thing and I refused to eat with it on. That first cat harness was pink, and that was the only good thing about it. When she pulled it off, it felt like my head was going to come off with it, and I learned to spin and snap at her when she grabbed it. Putting the harness on was a struggle, but taking it off was dangerous.

As I grew, so did the harnesses. They were all tourniquet-tight, though, and made me feel trapped. I didn't have to wear them all the time, but always for car rides and the front yard. The big-boy harness clicks at me when it fastens on. Why is it angry at me? Worse, one day my head came right off when she pulled off my harness. It was rolling around on the ground, but I still tried to bite the Farm

---

49   Other than what I accomplished in ten seconds while circling the landing, that is.

Manager while she reattached it.[50] Why did she keep trying to pull my head off? Suddenly one day there was a new harness. It took forever to put on because I kept trying to stick my head into it. It took weeks for me to figure out that there was no head-hole, and longer to stop flinching as she unclicked it off. This one didn't involve my head at all, but the buckle sounded like the old harness and it was clicking at me. Still, this step-in model was an acceptable harness, and I still use it today. So, that was the first trick I taught her; finding an un-scary harness. Not much of a trick, but harness time was the worst part of every day and now it's fixed.

When you come to visit, The Farm Manager will announce that I'm going to do some tricks for you. She is optimistic that I will spontaneously and flawlessly execute my trick routine, exactly the way I do it for her in the front yard. However, that is something we do in the front yard on the grass, which is *completely different* from the back yard on the deck. The Farm Manager is also a sloppy trainer, but I indulge her with a few quality tricks when we have company. I refuse to perform dumb tricks like "sit." So lame.

At first I didn't understand much English. The Farm Manager has this stick with a grungy pink tennis ball on the end and we play a game called "touch your nose." All I have to do is boop the ball. When she starts swinging it around, it gets more complicated, but if I keep my nose on the ball, I get treats. One good part about "touch your nose" is that I don't have to understand the spoken English, just the sign language she does when she's swinging that blasted stick around. After a while, though, I learn the words, too.

Seriously, the most boring trick in the world is Sit. It's easy and relaxing, though, so it's a good beginning trick. What I don't like is performing this one for an audience. Visitors are not impressed in the least, I mean, who is she fooling? It isn't a trick; it is, well, a normal boring thing that I do. Still, it is a mainstay of the repertoire, like it or not, and one of the ones we always do at the veterinary clinic. Maybe I should get one of those petitions started, lobby for some better material. After I get the corn reward. Corn-on-the-cob is my very favorite, so

---

50 Sorry, no video.

that is the bribe I am offered. It's the whole thing, too, husk and all, so there's a lot at stake. It's not like the miniature dog treats those fools will perform for. C'mon dogs, have some dignity! Join a union, stand up for your right to quality treats.

Lie Down is boring, too, but I can dress this one up quite a bit. It can go several ways. I can go with it, get my corn, and wander away. This is a good way keep to everyone's attention, when the tricks are so, you know, b-o-r-i-n-g. Then I look so darned clever when I brilliantly execute the next command. You have to know how to work the audience, especially when the only member in it is the Farm Manager. Another option is that I can ignore it, get comfortable and ignore "everyone" until they go away. Sometimes I even get the corn anyway. What I'm really supposed to do is the trick, get my corn treat, and wait attentively for the next trick. Since I'm already on the ground, the next trick we usually go for is Roll Over.

Don't get too excited about this one, though. Unlike a dog, you're not going to see me roll all the way over. There have been a couple capybaras who would roll over while swimming. I even did that once. But I'm not going roll all the way over on the ground. My brother, Caplin Rous, told me the world would come to an end if we rolled over, and I believe him. I'm certainly not going to be the one to push this poor planet over the edge. That's why I roll to the side, a gentle flop. You still get to see my tummy, which does *not* look like a hog belly, by the way. *Not at all.*

My favorite part about Roll Over is that visitors love to come over to rub my belly. I lie nice and still and they pet me and exclaim over my amazing fur, and sometimes I get pouffy, so my fur is amazing AND outstanding.[51] I am careful to wait until everyone is distracted and thinking what a mellow dude I am and then I *suddenly stand up!* It scares the heck out of everyone! I can really scatter a crowd! Nobody ever quite trusts me after that.

---

51 This is a test: What is it called when my fur sticks out? Jiminy cricket! It was only about four pages ago!

Stand Up is a classic trick that even Fat Bonnie, the rabbit, can do. The Farm Manager always asks me to do this one out in the open, though, and not anywhere that I can demonstrate the true utility of this skill. Indoors, I can rise up, rather like a scissor lift, and casually plant my elbows on the kitchen counter. Let's see your dog do that one! With practice, I think I could hop right over the kitchen barriers. By the time my elbows are on the counter, after all, it takes minimal effort to catapult the rest of the way over. I should give that a try the next time we have visitors.

One traditional trick I taught her a long time ago was Turn Around. Now this is a fine trick: it is cute, it is active and silly, and it can be very handy, like when we are on a narrow path and we need to turn around and go back. I turn around spontaneously for my corn, it is kind of a happy dance. I think dogs like this trick too. Even Fat Bonnie the rabbit does it for a nasty little dried-up blueberry, but she has "limited capacity" if you catch my drift. Anyway, my Turn Around for corn is what humans call "counter-clockwise," though I have seen clocks and I don't get the connection. Now, at dinnertime, and sometimes at breakfast, I turn around for my milk. Turn Around for milk is clockwise. There's a reason for this, but it's my secret and I'm not telling you.

Here's the ~~whole~~ story. The Farm Manager made me Turn Around for years, always with the corn treat, so I always did it counter-clockwise. She had corn in her hand, asked me to turn around, I turned around the corn way. No mystery there. Then she would yammer away at me, using all kinds of high falutin' words, twirling that dumb stick of hers. I could tell she was getting frustrated, and then we would move on to another trick. One day she said, "Turn Around the MILK way!" Oh, okay, that's easy enough. I know what the milk way is, I turn the other direction for milk. I can do that. So, I turned around the milk way, the yammering stopped and she said Good Boy a hundred times, and we moved onto the next trick. Now I do Turn Around the Corn Way, and Turn Around the Milk Way, both directions are covered, and we're getting along a lot better at trick time.

One of my favorite tricks is Wave Bye-Bye. I used to do a trick where we shake hands, but my feet are always muddy (or worse). The Farm Manager kept getting a muddy paw after shaking mine, so to keep her hand clean, she changed it so that I wave and don't touch anybody. For some reason, this is always my last trick, so it's my favorite. I always get to finish off the corn after the last trick.

Trick time was much better before she added the Ring Around the Rosy trick. It's an easy trick. I walk a circle around her, okay, I got it the first time. Duh. But it wasn't my idea. It's obviously an inferior trick. Plus, I'm walking around, no skill level required at all. Some performers would get mixed up with all this spinning and turning. I don't get mixed up, I get bored. Let's speed this up!

We're continually working on new tricks. Getting Pouffy is one. Sneeze is another one. I do that every night at milk time, anyway. We're working on Wiggle Your Ears, too. Those tricks are pretty unique to capybaras.[52] Some tricks we work on a lot, but never perform for visitors. They're too subtle, I guess. I know lots of my body parts, for instance. I know Foot, Ears, Eyeball. Remember, we did Eyeball for the veterinarian that time. She liked that a lot. The Farm Manager told me the vet was going to look at my eyeball, so I was prepared for her to be poking me in the eye. I didn't like it, but I wasn't surprised, either.

Sorry, the Doofus Dance is not available as a trick. The Prince does not dance on command.

Here's my last trick for you. It's usually the first one I do with the Farm Manager. Gimme a Kiss! You might think that everyone would want to do this trick with me, but it's pretty much a Farm Manager exclusive these days. Okay, are you ready? Here I come! Don't worry about my gigantic incisors, or the poop I ate five minutes ago or any of that. When I get enthusiastic I nearly break your nose! So, are you ready for a little peck on the cheek?

---

52   Okay, fine, hippos do the ear wiggle, too.

Chapter Six

Prince Dobalob Winnick

QUELLING THE RUMORS

Where do these ridiculous questions come from? Facebook, of course! Most of my friends are super nice. It's the "friends of friends" who are so hilarious with their comments like, "Capybaras taste like pork." Then when I get huffy about it and call them out for being rude, they sheepishly inform me that people commonly eat capybaras in South America. As if facts justify thoughtless comments.

So, what do capybaras taste like?

Okay, fine, let's set the record straight: yes, we do taste like pork! *Why do you want to know?* In Venezuela, for instance, we are ranched like little tiny water buffaloes. One of the less informed popes even declared us to be a fish so we could be eaten during Lent. That led to more ranching and a criminal amount of slaughter in the days leading up to Lent. We prefer Brazil, where we are adored and protected. Poaching in Brazil is subject to huge nasty fines, and it makes the national news when they nab someone for it. Brazilians take us very seriously. So if you are a capybara, I recommend a Rio vacation, and forget about Venezuela. Columbia is rumored to be a bad choice, too.

Capybaras are from Australia, right?

People are always trying to convince the Farm Manager that capybaras come from Australia. It's a bit insulting that they challenge her on this point, but, really? *Australia?* Marsupial-ville? We're a bit of an anomaly, but we are not marsupials. Get your oddities right, folks!

Capybaras will only poop in water.

Baby capybaras love to poop in shallow pans of water. No question about it. I did, almost all of us do. So convenient, from a pet-owner's standpoint, right? This is what *baby* capybaras do. Not all of us are so accommodating. I asserted myself by 5 months, and though I will still poop in water if the conditions are *perfect*, and I am talking about crystal clear bathwater temperature water, there are no guarantees. As an adult male capybara, I am serious about territorial marking, so *back off!* I poop anywhere I want to.

Capybaras can't run very fast. I mean, I could outrun one, right?

We are swift like the wind! Prey animals bolt when startled, rushing pell-mell for the exit. It is our best defense, and capybaras have been clocked at 30mph (48kph). Usain Bolt's top speed is 27.8mph (44.6kph). How fast are you? I was once spooked by a neighbor (Connor, again) peeking over the fence. I scrambled up my swimming pool steps and submerged myself in my pool before the Farm Manager figured out why I had been frightened! In fact, it was Connor who snuck up on us in the front yard the time I stampeded for my "safety corner," knocking the Farm Manager flat into the mud on my way past. He will verify my speed. Connor's one of my best buddies, but he does have a way of appearing out of nowhere. Don't forget the time I snagged my harness on a fence picket and busted the buckle. That was due to my astonishing speed.

Probably not a good idea to stick your hands right up to my face like that.

People seem to think that dogs like to sniff hands, but it's probably not a good idea to offer me your fingers. If you stick your fingers up to a hamster face, you're going to get bit. Pet rats, the rat under your house, you might hesitate to boop them on the nose. Rabbits don't like it. Beavers, porcupines, those are great big chompers at the front of their mouths, and those are wild animals anyway. (Oh yeah, like me.) Most people wouldn't consider offering them a hand to kiss. I'm a tame wild animal, and my Bucky Beavers are probably the biggest teeth you will ever see, plus I am always hungry. So, pat me on the back, pet me on the head, brush me, or best of all, rub something on my morrillo. That's the top of my nose, where I have a marking gland. There are no teeth up there.

So, you're like a dog, right? You go everywhere with the Farm Manager?

No. Prey animals are naturally wary and our comfort level rapidly disintegrates the farther we get from our home territory. When I was a baby and totally dependent upon the Farm Manager, I trusted her completely. We could go to the pet shop, to her office, or even to the cabin for a weekend. Like a human baby, I wasn't aware of many dangers, and riding in the car was interesting but not scary.

So, yeah, for about the first six months I was like a weird puppy. As I grew older, my awareness of my surroundings became more acute. My eyesight is designed for 360 degree viewing, not distance. This makes riding in the car an ordeal, and I get carsick and sweaty. At the same time, my sense of smell increased in importance. Being bombarded by oddball smells, first in the car ride, and then at the destination, is somewhat disconcerting. Diesel trucks, barking dogs, sirens and sudden stops, and worst of all, riding on the ferry. If I have to get out of the car, I tug at the harness and mark my path by dribbling urine down my back legs. This also washes the poop off my feet, the poop from the back seat of the car that I stepped in on the way out. This is exactly what it's like taking a dog places, right? I didn't think so.

Capybaras make awesome house pets. I saw a picture on the internet of a pet capybara sitting on a couch.

Oh, please. That's Melanie and Gari. Most of those guys you see on the internet are a few among hundreds, and besides they don't live in the house all the time. None of us do, at least the healthy ones don't. People occasionally have pet deer, too, and I see pictures of deer on people's couches, too. That doesn't make it normal, or good, or correct. That makes it a photo for the internet, and then that deer goes back outside. We are not house pets. Heck, I haven't sat on our couch since 2009.

Where can I buy a capybara? I bet there's lots of good information on the internet.

There are several capybara breeders in the USA. You will quickly discover that there isn't much information at all on the internet. Once you start doing some serious research—more than reading this book, for crying out loud—you will discover that the capybara community is very small. The worst thing I could do is to encourage anyone to buy a capybara before they truly understand what they are getting into. Our little community isn't set up to rescue huge quantities of cast-off adolescent capybaras.

Is your name Dobbye or Doobie or Dobie?

My name is Dobby. A dobby is a kind of loom with a special dobby attachment. The dobby part creates a fancy woven strip, often in a geometric pattern like chevrons. Western style shirts often have a dobby pattern repeated in strips at intervals among the plaid pattern threads. It's very fancy, like my fur. When the Farm Manager hollers at me, people think she is yelling "Doggy!" That fools them every time!

Why is there meloxicam in my milk? Isn't gabapentin a pain medication?

How astute! You get points for that one! That's because of my fractured L7 vertebrae. That is a fancy way of saying I have a broken back. The messed up part is way back there where my legs attach so I have a hard time walking, especially on stairs. I have good days and bad days, but all that calcium added to my milk should help me heal. I also have my own UV lights to help me absorb that calcium. I'm currently getting k-laser treatments to enhance healing, and those seem to be helping. It could take months before I am perfect again, but that's the plan.

FAME AND FORTUNE

For a spectacular and royal creature, I am not terribly interested in fame and fortune. My brother, Caplin, was the World's Most Famous Capybara. He's probably still the most famous capybara, a television star and everything. We weren't littermates. He was born a year and a half before me, but to the same parents, Bonnie and Clyde. Did you check out that video of me before I came to live here? That's Caplin! He's the big capybara clicking at me for getting all the attention. I know they were love clicks. That's the only time we met, but he was really important in my life. You see, it was Caplin who started this whole capybara craze. Okay, Capyboppy was first, but he didn't even have a Facebook page! Seriously, if Caplin hadn't broken the capybara-as-pets ice, the Farm Manager might never have looked for me.

So, you can imagine my surprise when I discovered I was running for President of the United States![53] There I was, in the September 5, 2016 issue of *The New Yorker* magazine, alongside Hillary and Donald! I honestly have no idea when the paparazzi took a photo of me drinking a beer, but I was ready to drink another one when I saw that picture! That is the kind of publicity I do not need. In fact, I did not win the presidency, much to the disappointment of my several fans. I am spared the indignity of wearing diapers in the prissy and undoubtedly sanitary White House, the embarrassment of slurping my milk in front of cabinet secretaries, and the bitter disappointment of the south lawn quality. It is very pretty grass, but it is without a doubt soaked in herbicides and pesticides, as are all lawns of that caliber. Perfectly inedible. There probably isn't a single dandelion anywhere on the White House grounds. There is a lovely rose garden, though. I have eaten ours down to the dirt, but the White House roses could probably last me through two terms!

Because I live in a quiet suburban neighborhood (quiet except for noisy Norman the goose, and the Boeing test flights that buzz the house.) I don't want too many people learning that I am royalty. The parking lot in front of the house is too small to accommodate thundering hordes of admirers. I wouldn't mind getting the extra corn, though. Funny thing is, I seem to have a fairly steady stream of visitors. That's how I landed my current job. I am the Director of Fundraising at Stacy's Funny Farm.

---

53 The Farm Manager long ago posted a photo of me standing up in the kitchen with my paws up on the gate, looking just like Barry Blitt's drawing: http://www.newyorker.com/magazine/2016/09/05/hillary-clinton-and-donald-trumps-latest-polls

STACY'S FUNNY FARM

You might have noticed all the freeloaders around here. That whole Garden Party crew, for instance. Wastrels, all of them. It's even worse indoors. First of all, I have to share my puny kitchen area with all sorts of birds. That is an improvement over the chinchilla, guinea pigs, hamster and gerbil that were there when I arrived. I pretty much got rid of those deadbeats. The birds remain. Old Jorge the cockatiel will live to annoy us until the end of time. His old buddy, Vincent, will broadcast every conceivable event until then. The cage full of budgies is hard to ignore, so loud! Oh, wait. It's only one tiny bird, Spitfire the budgie. There's also a couple handicapped doves in here, now. There still are a few guinea pigs and even a couple rats in another room. Where do they all come from?

Unlike me—I was planned—almost all of these guys ended up here because no one else wanted them. The hens are old and don't lay eggs too often. Princess Blur the banty Mille Fleur hen was loud, lonely, and obnoxious and so she fits right in here. The useless drakes fight all the time. Their previous owners couldn't deal with that, so they fight here, instead. Norman and the Farm Manager deal with them every spring. We have some girl ducks, too, but not too many. There's a big domed flight cage full of doves nobody wanted. There's a pigeon in there, too. We have a turtle. A rabbit. There are even two big old mean tomcats. No dogs, please! I am the biggest pet and it's going to stay that way!

People have always brought hand-me-down pets to the Farm Manager to take care of. She's a real pushover. She's been that way for about forty-five years. When people come to visit me, that's when they notice the other moochers. It's hard to miss the cages in the kitchen behind me, and if Norman is honking out back, that is kind of distracting, too. The interesting thing is that recently my visitors started to leave donations. Not for me, but for the other pets. So now we are a non-profit organization, I mean an official one. There's never any profit to be made by feeding fifty freeloaders. I don't mean to brag, but every donation that comes in is because of me. I am so irresistible!

ASK DOBBY

I don't know what else to say. I think you're ready to take the quiz! It's an open book test. Take your time. Remember, *nobody* cares about your score. You can work with a group; heck, you can cheat all you want. If you have trouble answering any of the questions, ask me! Seriously, you can come to my website and ask: https://petcapybara.com/ask-dobby/

Chapter Seven

THE QUIZ: ARE YOU READY FOR A CAPYBARA?

Most of you aren't seriously considering a pet capybara, but a disturbing number of newbie capybara enthusiasts decide to get one as soon as they learn of our existence. We are tame wild animals, not domestic pets, and we don't want to see a lot of us showing up in rescues, do we?

The Farm Manager has been keeping track of pet capybaras, and at this writing she knows of about eighty-five in the US and Canada, distributed among about sixty owners. (At least five of those capybaras are rescues.) That isn't very many because this is uncharted territory. Capybara owners are cutting edge, or another way to put it is clueless. Each one of them feels they have the answers and are approaching it correctly. Sixty different owners and sixty different opinions. Twice that many opinions if you ask the spouses, too!

Now that you have read my book, you have a lot of insights into one individual who is a very spoiled royal capybara. Are you ready to tackle your own little monster? This isn't like one of those regular online quizzes, where you tally your score and discover you are 73% ready to move to Saturn if we kill Earth. Consider this a glimpse into Dobby's World, an adventure into the reality of keeping a pet capybara like me happy. And, hopefully, alive.

Duh, this silly quiz is optional. If you have no shame, skip ahead to the so-called answers. I promise you, nobody cares. I will tell you that this quiz has been out for a while, and I haven't received much flack from the capybara community about it. They did request that I add the "How old are you?" question. The Farm Manager is already ancient, and she will be lucky to outlive me. I can't allow myself to consider what I would do without her.

You have my permission to write in this book. Please, no mustaches and no coloring. Do you have a pencil and eraser? Don't turn the page until you are ready!

DOBBY'S WORLD QUIZ

1. Are you legally allowed to have a capybara where you live?

    a. I have absolutely no idea!

    b. My country allows private individuals to own a capybara

    c. My state allows private individuals to own a capybara

    d. My county allows private individuals to own a capybara

    e. My city allows private individuals to own a capybara

    f. My homeowner's association (or CC&R's) allows individuals to own a capybara

    g. I am an exempt or licensed petting zoo

    h. I am an AZA certified zoo

2. What kind of animal experience do you have?

    a. I have never owned a pet

    b. I have had cats and dogs

    c. I have had several pets from this list: hamsters, rats, mice, gerbils, guinea pigs, budgies, cockatiels, doves or pigeons, finches, outdoor rabbits, chickens, tropical fish

    d. I have had several pets from this list: house rabbits, ferrets, chinchillas, degus, sugar gliders, hedgehogs, ducks, geese, goats, potbellied pigs, saltwater aquarium, parrots

    e. I have had one or more of these pets: horse, raccoon, opossum, macaw, cockatoo, full grown iguana, other large exotic bird/animal, or special needs bird/animal

3. Are you afraid of animals that bite?

  a. Yes, and I have small children

  b. Yes, but I can overcome my fear by starting with a baby animal

  c. Not really, but my experience includes only domestic animals

  d. Not really, but do all capybaras bite?

  e. No, do you want to see my scars?

4. Do you have the support of your family for this long-term project?

  a. I have a child/children under the age of 12 or I live alone

  b. I have a partner/family, but they will not be involved in this project

  c. My partner is supportive and we will not be starting a family for a couple more years

  d. My partner/family is supportive, expects to take part in some aspects of care

  e. My partner/family, veterinarian, and pet sitter are well informed and remain totally committed to this project

5. How much time can you devote to this pet?

  a. I'm pretty booked up but I can find time.

  b. I have little kids, so I'm home all the time, anyway.

  c. I have a couple of dogs already, so adding time for a capybara is no big deal.

  d. I work 12 hour shifts so I have lots of days off.

  e. I work full time, but I'm single, so I have lots of time for a pet.

  f. I work from home, so I'm here all the time.

  g. I work part time.

h. I am a trust fund baby. I don't work.

6. What kind of exotic animal care experience do you have? How about your partner?

a. I have a cat

b. I have a house rabbit

c. I have volunteered at a zoo or aquarium

d. I work as a vet tech or I have a horse

e. I work as a vet tech for an exotic animal veterinarian

f. I own an exotic pet shop

g. I operate a small petting zoo

h. I am a veterinarian, exotic animal breeder, or zookeeper

7. How agile are you? Can you still manage a flying tackle?

a. Why do you ask?

b. I am handicapped, and not able to respond quickly.

c. I'm pretty active, but I'm usually wearing the wrong shoes for tackling capybaras.

d. I can manage if I have to.

e. I'm in respectable condition for my age.

f. I'm in great shape, not a problem.

8. What will your capybara do while you are at work or away?

a. It can stay in the basement while I am away

b. It's going to run around the house, watch daytime soaps

c. The neighbor can see it from their window

d. My kids can play with it when they get home from school

e. My wife says she will feed it

f. My dog walker will come every day

g. I work from home

h. I don't work

9. What will you do with your capybara when you go on vacation?

a. I will take it with me

b. My husband doesn't travel with me and can stay home with the capybara

c. My adult brother/grown son will come by daily to feed it

d. My adult sister/grown daughter will come stay with it

e. Isn't that what pet sitters are for?

f. My pet sitter has agreed to give it a try

g. My pet sitter has exotic animal experience

h. I don't take vacations

10. Does your veterinarian have exotic animal experience?

a. I don't have a veterinarian

b. I have a veterinarian for my dog/cat

c. I will be able to find an exotic vet in my area

d. I have a veterinarian for my rabbit/guinea pig/exotic animal

e. My veterinarian knows I am getting a capybara and is very supportive

f. I am a veterinarian

11. In an emergency, can you come up with a wrangler?

a. I can get my capybara to the vet alone

b. There are some kids across the street who can help

c. I have a grown son living nearby

d. My neighbors are generally pretty good with livestock

e. I have hired help around all the time

12. Do you have adequate housing for a capybara?

a. I live at my parent's house

b. I have an apartment.

c. I own a condominium with a patio

d. I own my urban home and we have an alley

e. I own my suburban home and it has a little back yard

f. I own my suburban home and it has a huge yard

g. I own my rural home with a huge yard.

h. I own my rural home on acreage.

i. I own my farm, have acreage and a barn.

13. Is your home capybara-ready?

a. What do you mean?

b. How is it different from cat-proofing a house?

c. We already have dogs, so it is all set up with a dog door

    d. All power cords are covered for safety

    e. The house plants will be removed

14. **Not all capybaras are well behaved enough to live in a house. Very often they will begin to mark the floor with urine at about 5-6 months, and by a year, they can become territorial and mark with feces. It is at this point that they may become aggressive toward a family member. Do you have a "Plan B" for housing your capybara if it becomes territorial in this way?**

    a. Capybaras are a good investment: we would make money if we sold ours at that point.

    b. A well-trained capybara is housebroken. The Farm Manager is a lousy trainer.

    c. We are dedicated capybara owners. We will rip out the carpets, sell the furniture, let the capybaras take over, and hope the bank doesn't notice before the mortgage is paid off.

    d. Our home has an area we can isolate for the capybara so he can still come into the house.

    e. We are prepared to keep our capybara outdoors if that is what he wants.

    f. Capybaras are outdoor animals. Once ours is big enough to live outdoors, he'll move out.

15. **Do you live in a "capybara friendly" climate? That would be about 60-95F degrees (15-35C) with lots of rain.**

    a. I live in Florida

    b. I live in the South

    c. I live in the Southwest

    d. I live in the Northeast

e. I live in the Midwest

f. I live in the Pacific Northwest

g. I live in Canada

h. I live in _____ but I have a heated barn near the house.

16. Do you have suitable outdoor space for a capybara?

a. My capybara will be an indoor pet.

b. I have no secure outdoor space.

c. My back yard is mostly fenced

d. I live next door to a park or school

e. My capybara yard is fully fenced with 4' high chain link fencing

f. My capybara yard is fully fenced with 6' high sight-obscuring secure fencing

g. Delivery people do not pass through the secured capybara yard.

h. My capybara yard is double gated for security.

17. Where will your baby capybara sleep?

a. Outdoors, with the dogs/sheep

b. Outdoors, in its own pen

c. In the garage

d. In the house, in a secure area

e. In the house, wherever it wants to

f. In our bed!

18. **Baby capybaras readily use a shallow pan of water for a toilet. It can get a little messy and, of course, carrying a large shallow pan of filthy water through the house to a dumping location has drawbacks. Where will yours be located?**

    a. In the kitchen

    b. In the hallway

    c. In the laundry room

    d. In the mud room/back porch

    e. In the guest bathroom

    f. In the kid's bathroom

    g. In the master bathroom

    h. Outside

19. **Is your yard safe for a capybara?**

    a. It has been more than two years since any herbicide or pesticide has been used in my yard

    b. My dogs have never eaten anything toxic out there

    c. My capybara will not have access to rhododendrons, azaleas, or other toxic plants

    d. My yard has no toxic plants that I know of

    e. I have fenced off the toxic plants

    f. I have had a consultant over to evaluate my yard for toxic plants, which I then removed

20. Capybaras are herd animals. How do you propose to supply a herd for your capybara?

a. I will be his playmate

b. We have a dog he can play with

c. We have goats he can live with

d. I can supply him with many activities and amusements throughout the day

e. We have geese, ducks, and chickens he can play with

f. We are getting two or more capybaras

21. Can you fit a bale of hay into your vehicle?

a. A what? Doesn't that make a huge mess?

b. I don't think I can buy hay anywhere around here

c. I think it will fit in the trunk of my Camry

d. I can borrow a truck

e. I've put worse things in my car

f. I have a truck/van/SUV

g. I'll have everything delivered

22. Is your vehicle interior indestructible?

a. What are you talking about?

b. My capy can ride in the back of my truck with the dogs

c. I am ready to sacrifice my only car to my capybara

d. My car is already ruined

e. I have a spare car I can sacrifice

23. How much extra space do you have in your refrigerator?

  a. A quart of yogurt

  b. 25 pounds of vegetables and apples

  c. A case of 24 heads of romaine

  d. A box of 48 fresh corn-on-the-cob

  e. All of the above

24. What's in your pocket besides your cell phone?

  a. What are pockets?

  b. Lipstick and powder. You meant my purse, right?

  c. My wallet and a dirty handkerchief

  d. Car keys

  e. Swiss Army knife

  f. Duct tape

  g. Cable ties, some bits of rusty chicken wire, pieces of string too short to use, and part of a plastic bag

25. What is your life expectancy?

  a. 1—5 years

  b. 5—10 years

  c. 10—15 years

  d. 15—20 years

That's the end! Did you mark your answers? Remember, no mustaches and no coloring!

THE SO-CALLED ANSWERS

I warned you that there are no real answers, and until people have kept capybaras as pets for a few more decades, we're not likely to see any consensus. For this quiz, I made up the questions and I am making up the answers, too. It is completely based upon my priorities, and my royal opinions. I am one big, grubby male capybara, and that's the extent of my personal experience. This quiz is completely devoid of scientific basis. So, let's not take it too seriously, okay?

Point score is after each answer. Go ahead and tally your points and then I'll give you a meaningless score at the end. Complain directly to Ask Dobby. The website address for that is hidden on page 140.

1. Are you legally allowed to have a capybara where you live?

   a. I have absolutely no idea! 0

   b. My country allows private individuals to own a capybara 1

   c. My state allows private individuals to own a capybara 1

   d. My county allows private individuals to own a capybara 2

   e. My city allows private individuals to own a capybara 3

   f. My homeowner's association (or CC&R's) allows individuals to own a capybara 3

   g. I am an exempt or licensed petting zoo 4

   h. I am an AZA certified zoo 4

If you don't know the legal status of exotic ownership in your location, your pet may be confiscated. It has happened. Then the state is caring for your capybara, with all their vast know-how regarding exotic animals. If you live in a city and your pet bites someone, or even a dog, your capybara may be confiscated, even if it is legal for you to have one. That has happened, too.

2. What kind of animal experience do you have?

a. I have never owned a pet 0 *major fail,* subtract all previous and subsequent points

b. I have had cats and dogs 1

c. I have had several pets from this list: hamsters, rats, mice, gerbils, guinea pigs, budgies, cockatiels, doves or pigeons, finches, outdoor rabbits, chickens, tropical fish 2

d. I have had several pets from this list: house rabbits, ferrets, chinchillas, degus, sugar gliders, hedgehogs, ducks, geese, goats, pot bellied pigs, saltwater aquarium, parrots 3

e. I have had one of these pets: horse, raccoon, kinkajou, macaw, cockatoo, full grown Iguana, other large exotic bird/animal, or special needs bird/animal 4

We are gigantic wild animals that can become aggressive. Some of us are gentle teddy bears, others are NOT. We don't always get along with other animals or humans. We have a finicky digestive system, like a guinea pig, rabbit, or even a horse. Young capybaras can suddenly drop dead from severe gastric distress. This is not a beginner animal. I have almost died three times.

3. Are you afraid of animals that bite?

a. Yes, and I have small children 0

b. Yes, but I can overcome my fear by starting with a baby animal 1

c. Not really, but my experience includes only domestic animals 2

 d. Not really, but do all capybaras bite? 3

 e. No, do you want to see my scars? 5

Capybaras bite. Capybara owners get bitten. We have big, razor sharp teeth, and biting is our only defense, other than running away. If you are afraid of getting bit, capybaras are a poor pet choice.

4. Do you have the support of your family for this long-term project?

 a. I have a child/children under the age of 12 or I live alone 1

 b. I have a partner/family, but they will not be involved in this project 1

 c. My partner is supportive and we will not be starting a family for a couple more years 2

 d. My partner/family is supportive, expects to take part in some aspects of care 3

 e. My partner/family, veterinarian, and pet sitter are well informed and remain totally committed to this project 5

Capybaras are tame wild animals, not domestic animals. Kids are unpredictable and move quickly and make me nervous. By the time I was about 6 months old, I began to show marked preferences for certain family members, and hostility toward others. I was savvy enough to be wary of strangers, while making quick value judgments: friend, lover, or enemy? A 125-pound pet capybara can quickly dominate even the most informal get-togethers. As for family support, without The Bartender, the Farm Manager would never get a break. We are adorable for the first six months, cute as the devil up to a year, and a full-time job from then on. Remember, even taking us to the vet is a two-person endeavor.

5. How much time can you devote to this pet?

 a. I'm pretty booked up but I can find time. 0

 b. I have little kids, so I'm home all the time, anyway. 0

c. I have a couple of dogs already, so adding time for a capybara is no big deal. 1

d. I work 12-hour shifts so I have lots of days off. 1

e. I work full time, but I'm single, so I have lots of time for a pet. 2

f. I work from home, so I'm here all the time. 3

g. I work part time. 4

h. I am a trust fund baby. I don't work. 5

Baby capybaras are tiny and quite fragile. They are too little to be left outside on their own, but if they don't get outdoors enough, they won't get enough Vitamin D. Too little Vitamin D, they can't absorb enough calcium, and they get rickets. They need to eat fresh grass, fruits, and vegetables to get enough Vitamin C. Too little Vitamin C and they get scurvy. Dry hay has no Vitamin C, so young capybaras being raised indoors on hay in the winter aren't getting enough of either vitamin. I have seen the results of vitamin deficiency (his name was Garibaldi) and it isn't pretty. "Somebody" needs to sit outdoors with your baby capybara while it grazes, so set aside a few hours a day for this purpose.

6. What kind of exotic animal care experience do you have? How about your partner?

a. I have a cat. 0

b. I have a house rabbit. 1

c. I have volunteered at a zoo or aquarium 2 points for each year, do the math

d. I work as a vet tech or I have a horse. 3

e. I work as a vet tech for an exotic animal veterinarian. 4

f. I own an exotic pet shop. 4

g. I operate a small petting zoo. 5

    h. I am a veterinarian, exotic animal breeder, or zookeeper. 6

A cat or dog is not adequate pre-capybara experience. You are getting closer with a house rabbit. Horses are even more challenging, expensive and time-consuming. The Farm Manager had a pet raccoon and vole when she was 20 and hasn't cared for fewer than 30 pets (at once) since 1990. Capybaras are not "beginner" pets.

7. How agile are you? Can you still manage a flying tackle?

    a. Why do you ask? 0

    b. I am handicapped, and not able to respond quickly. 0

    c. I'm pretty active, but I'm usually wearing the wrong shoes for tackling capybaras. 1

    d. I can manage if I have to. 2

    e. I'm in respectable condition for my age. 3

    f. I'm in great shape, not a problem. 4

The Bartender asked me to include this question. Having watched the Farm Manager tackle me more than once, he can't believe I almost overlooked this aspect of capybara care. You have to be ready for anything.

8. What will your capybara do while you are at work (or away)?

    a. It can stay in the basement while I am away. 0

    b. It's going to run around the house, watch daytime soap. 0

    c. The neighbor can see it from their window. 0

    d. My kids can play with it after they get home from school. 0

    e. My wife says she will feed it. 1

    f. My dog walker will come every day. 2

    g. I work from home. 4

    h. I don't work. 5

We are intelligent, curious animals. Would you give a monkey free range of your home while you are not there? Your house will surely be destroyed and/or we will find something dangerous to eat. We need a warm safe area with food, water, and potty bowl, preferably outdoors. I learned to toss my water bowl fairly early on, though I never tossed my potty bowl. (Well, I toss them now, but they are outdoors.) Do you want a capybara or not? If you don't want to hang out with me all day, get a more appropriate pet, like a guppy.

9. What will you do with your capybara when you go on vacation?

    a. I will take it with me. 1

    b. My husband doesn't travel with me and can stay home with the capybara. 2

    c. My adult brother/grown son will come by daily to feed it. 2

    d. My adult sister/grown daughter will come stay with it. 3

    e. Isn't that what pet sitters are for? 3

    f. My pet sitter has agreed to give it a try. 4

    g. My pet sitter has exotic animal experience. 5

    h. I don't take vacations. 5

The Farm Manager has trouble finding pet sitters who can deal with ordinary chickens. My current sitter has nerves of steel, but when my humans go on vacation the Farm Manager leaves me fenced out of the kitchen so that he can care for me and the kitchen birds without being in direct contact with me. Another time, I was so upset when the Farm Manager left me that I bit my human sister, even though I really like her. She won't sit for me anymore, though I have since forgiven her. Remember the story about taking me to the cabin?

Don't assume you can travel with your capybara unless you are joining a circus.

10. Does your veterinarian have exotic animal experience?

a. I don't have a veterinarian. 0

b. I have a veterinarian for my dog/cat. 1

c. I will be able to find an exotic vet in my area. 2

d. I have a veterinarian for my rabbit/guinea pig/exotic animal. 3

e. My veterinarian knows I am getting a capybara and is very supportive. 4

f. I am a veterinarian. 5

My veterinarian knew about me before the Farm Manager brought me home, so he wasn't at all surprised when a capybara made an appointment. You will definitely want your veterinarian to examine your pet capybara as soon as it comes home. This is to determine a baseline of temperature, weight, and general health. Because I did this, Dr. F was able to treat me when I became seriously ill about a week later. He saved my life. Surprising an unknown veterinarian in a 24-hour emergency clinic with a sick capybara is not going to result in a positive outcome.

11. In an emergency, can you come up with a wrangler?

a. I can get my capybara to the vet alone. 0

b. There are some kids across the street who can help. 0

c. I have a grown son living nearby. 2

d. My neighbors are generally pretty good with livestock. 3

e. My partner is usually around here somewhere. 4

f. I have hired help around all the time. 5

Once your capybara is about 6 months old, getting it to do anything it doesn't want to do will take two people. It is safe to assume that if your capybara is injured, the last thing it will want to do is put on a harness and get in the car. Safe wrangling takes two people, one to drive, one to manage the animal. One time, I refused to get out of the car for three hours. It's funny now, because we were doing a trial run to the new clinic. But three hours? Yep.

12. Do you have adequate housing for a capybara?

 a. I live at my parent's house. 0

 b. I have an apartment. 0

 c. I own a condominium with a patio. 0

 d. I own my urban home and we have an alley. 0

 e. I own my suburban home and it has a little back yard. 1

 f. I own my suburban home and it has a huge yard 2

 g. I own my rural home with a huge yard. 3

 h. I own my rural home on acreage. 4

 i. I own my farm, have acreage and a barn. 5

Tame capybaras may be able to tolerate coming into your house briefly, or to sleep, but they cannot thrive indoors. Young capybaras need to be outdoors or they do not get enough Vitamin D, which can lead to low bone density. Capybaras need to graze, so you will need pasture, and they need to swim. In cold climates, they will need shelter and being prone to frostbite, they need to be able to get out of snow and off frozen ground. If you do not own your property, there is no guarantee that you will be allowed to make the accommodations necessary to maintain your capybara's health.

13. Is your home capybara-ready?

    a. What do you mean? 0

    b. How is it different from cat-proofing a house? 1

    c. We already have dogs, so it is all set up with a dog door. 2

    d. All power cords are covered for safety. 3

    e. The house plants will be removed. 4

One of my favorite photos is of my brother, Caplin Rous, standing on a table in the middle of a great big puzzle-in-progress! We can stand way up tall and reach anything, we are surprisingly good jumpers, and we can be rather belligerent if you try to separate us from a "project." We are notorious for biting through cords and can sever one faster than an electrician. I have never seen a dog door, but it sounds delicious! Anyway, capybaras are oversized beavers in your house chewing everything up.

14. Not all capybaras are well behaved enough to live in a house. Very often they will begin to mark the floor with urine at about 5-6 months, and by a year, they can become territorial and mark with feces. It is at this point that they may become aggressive toward a family member. Do you have a "Plan B" for housing your capybara if it becomes territorial in this way?

    a. Capybaras are a good investment: we would make money if we sold ours at that point. 0

    b. A well-trained capybara is housebroken. The Farm Manager is a lousy trainer. 0

    c. We are dedicated capybara owners. We will rip out the carpets, sell the furniture, let the capybaras take over, and hope the bank doesn't notice before the mortgage is paid off. 5

    d. Our home has an area we can isolate for the capybara so he can still come into the house. 3

e. We are prepared to keep our capybara outdoors if that is what he wants. 4

f. Capybaras are outdoor animals. Once ours is big enough to live outdoors, he'll move out. 5

Most people with pet capybaras keep them outdoors, contrary to the prevailing myth. I know of very few full grown capybaras that live in (or have access to) a normally furnished home, and they usually belong to an extraordinary trainer. It didn't work out for grubby old me, and the other indoor capybaras you see frequently on the Internet are either very ill, very young, or are not living in a typically furnished home.

15. Do you live in a "capybara friendly" climate? That would be about 60-95F degrees (15-35C) with lots of rain.

a. I live in Florida. 4

b. I live in the South. 3

c. I live in the Southwest. 3

d. I live in the Northeast. 2

e. I live in the Midwest. 1

f. I live in the Pacific Northwest. 2

g. I live in Canada. 1

h. I live in _____ but I have a heated barn near the house. 4

The premier capybara breeder was in Arkansas, not exactly a tropical climate. With care, capys can live anywhere they have access to bathing water and heated winter shelter. We develop skin problems in hot dry climates, and the ROUS Foundation has recorded more deaths from frostbite induced infections than I thought possible. You must be able to build the accommodations you need to keep your capybara healthy. That is why you need to own your home, not rent.

16. Do you have suitable outdoor space for a capybara?

a. My capybara will be an indoor pet. 0

b. I have no secure outdoor space. 0

c. My back yard is mostly fenced. 0

d. I live next door to a park or school. 0

e. My capybara yard is fully fenced with 4' high chain link fencing. 1

f. My capybara yard is fully fenced with 6' high sight-obscuring secure fencing. 2

g. Delivery people do not pass through the secured capybara yard. 3

h. My capybara yard is double gated for security. 4

One pet capybara needs at least 1,000 sf of secured grazing pasture, which is not the same as a pretty lawn that has been chemically fertilized or had "weed & feed" on it. We also need a swimming pool or at least a very large stock tank. Wading pools are cute toys for young capybaras. Capybaras tend to go walkabout if not securely fenced, often with deadly consequences. The ROUS Foundation has seen that happen, too.

17. Where will your baby capybara sleep?

a. Outdoors, with the dogs/sheep. 3

b. Outdoors, in its own pen. 4

c. In the garage. 0

d. In the house, in a secure area. 2

e. In the house, wherever it wants to. 0

f. In our bed! 1

Capybaras are creatures of habit. Choose wisely and think through the consequences of your sleeping arrangement. If your capybara is ill or recovering from surgery can you accommodate him? How will his bedroom function when the pet sitter has to care for him? Will your pet sitter be able to feed your dogs safely if your capybara shares living quarters with them? Will you still want her in your bed when she weighs 140 pounds and startles at the sound of 4th of July fireworks?

18. **Baby capybaras readily use a shallow pan of water for a toilet. It can get a little messy and, of course, carrying a large shallow pan of filthy water through the house to a dumping location has drawbacks. Where will yours be located?**

   a. In the kitchen 0

   b. In the hallway 0

   c. In the laundry room 1

   d. In the mud room/back porch 4

   e. In the guest bathroom 2

   f. In the kid's bathroom 1

   g. In the master bathroom 3

   h. Outside 4

Capybaras, like guinea pigs, are prolific pooping machines. Baby capybaras typically use a shallow pan of water for a potty bowl, and most continue in this fashion until they are about 6 months old. At that point, a few continue with the potty bowl but most graduate to outdoor hard surfaces. Carrying a loaded shallow potty bowl through the house to a dumping place is not recommended. Locate your potty near a toilet, preferably in a bathroom with little traffic and where the door can be propped open, night and day. Trust me, your guests will love to share a bathroom with a capybara! Don't even think about disposing the prolific poop in your yard, there is too much! Figure about a quart (liter) a day for a 110-pound (50kg) capybara. I am a prince, so I have my own outdoor bathroom!

19. Is your yard safe for a capybara?

a. It has been more than two years since any herbicide or pesticide has been used in my yard. 1

b. My dogs have never eaten anything toxic out there. 0

c. My capybara will not have access to rhododendrons, azaleas, or other toxic plants. 2

d. My yard has no toxic plants that I know of. 1

e. I have fenced off the toxic plants. 3

f. I have had a consultant over to evaluate my yard for toxic plants, which I then removed. 4

The community loses more young capybaras to toxic plant poisoning than any other single cause. We will eat anything. A shocking number of house plants are toxic, so watch out for those, too. Older capybaras seem to be more discriminating, but we are very trusting and may assume anything accessible to us has been approved for capy consumption.

20. Capybaras are herd animals. How do you propose to supply a herd for your capybara?

a. I will be his playmate. 1

b. We have a dog he can play with. 2

c. We have goats he can live with. 0

d. I can supply him with many activities and amusements throughout the day. 3

e. We have geese, ducks, and chickens he can play with. 3

f. We are getting two or more capybaras. 4

I am a big believer in the value of enrichment. Even if you intend to be your capybara's best friend, you are not likely to spend 24 hours a day with him. I spend a good part of every afternoon with the Farm Manager, but I am a remarkably self-sufficient capybara. I have ducks and chickens but they aren't out with me all of the time. There is wildlife all over my yard, and I have access to the house all day. I have toys to rub my nose on, a selection of pools, balls to play with, and a predictable succession of snacks throughout the day. While it is true that I am obsessively bonded to the Farm Manager, I am very busy and don't always have time to bother her. Some capybaras love dogs, and even cats, but I don't think I would want a goat to be head-butting me all day. That would make me mad. I probably wouldn't like to live with another male capybara, either. That doesn't seem to work out too well.

21. Can you fit a bale of hay into your vehicle?

a. A what? Doesn't that make a huge mess? 0

b. I don't think I can buy hay anywhere around here. 0

c. I think it will fit in the trunk of my Camry. 1

d. I can borrow a truck. 2

e. I've put worse things in my car. 3

f. I have a truck/van/SUV. 4

g. I'll have everything delivered. 4

Once you put a bale of hay in your car, you will forever be finding bits of hay everywhere. Plus, hay bales are bigger than they look. In the Pacific Northwest, uncovered pickup truck beds have limited utility: hay gets soaked with rain by the time you get home. Do I need to mention that you need a hay storage area at home? Having it delivered indicates that you have your financial priorities skewed toward capybara care. Good for you.

22. Is your vehicle interior indestructible?

    a. What are you talking about? 0

    b. My capy can ride in the back of my truck with the dogs. 0

    c. I am ready to sacrifice my only car to my capybara. 3

    d. My car is already ruined. 4

    e. I have a spare car I can sacrifice. 5

Some capybaras are well behaved in the car, but if they get spooked, accidents can happen. One baby got his leg caught and broke it. As long as your capy fits into a carrier, use it. Obviously, a capybara in the back of a truck needs to be in a carrier because, duh! A full grown capy is unlikely to get into a carrier without some serious training, and anyway you won't be able to lift the carrier with a full-grown capybara inside. You'll want to line your car with multiple layers of blankets for quick cleanups. You also need to install a pet car barrier to keep your capy off your lap while you're driving. Duct tape comes in many colors, now, and you'll be able find one that matches your car interior to fix the bite marks in your vinyl. Seat belts can be replaced.

23. How much extra space do you have in your refrigerator?

    a. A quart of yogurt 0

    b. 25 pounds of vegetables and apples 1

    c. A case of 24 heads of romaine 2

    d. A box of 48 fresh corn-on-the-cob 2

    e. All of the above 5

I have my own refrigerator, and when corn and lettuce deliveries happen on the same day, it overflows into the upstairs refrigerator. Which is already full of guinea pig food. Corn and romaine lettuce fills the main space in the refrigerator. The drawers and door spaces will hold a couple weeks' worth of apples, pears, and potatoes.

24. What's in your pocket besides your cell phone?

a. What are pockets? 0

b. Lipstick and powder. You meant my purse, right? 0

c. My wallet and a dirty handkerchief 1

d. Car keys 1

e. Swiss Army knife 2

f. Duct tape 3

g. Cable ties, some bits of rusty chicken wire, pieces of string too short to use, and part of a plastic bag 4

This is a lifestyle question. You need to be prepared for anything. We are not designer pets. Let's all hope we never see a capybara in Paris Hilton's handbag. Or as Paris Hilton's handbag.

25. What is your own life expectancy?

a. 1—5 years 0

b. 5—10 years 1

c. 10—15 years 2

d. 15—20 years 5

In the wild, capybaras over 4 years old are rarely found. In zoos, they may live 10-12 years if well cared for. In captivity, they can live to 15-18 years if the owners know what they are doing. If you are over 60 years old, you really want to think about whether you will outlive your pet.

Now, tally up your points and divide by the number of questions, 25. I know you're going to want to know how you did so here you go, pretend you are back in high school. Keep in mind that this quiz has absolutely no credibility, and a top score does not win you a capybara!

3.7 + ...A   You get it and your lifestyle could be capybara compatible.

2.7—3.6......B   You get the idea, but you probably need to make some major adjustments.

1.7—2.6......C   You need to do a LOT more research.

1.0—1.6......D   You took the quiz for fun, right?

0.9—0 ....F   You have never seen a live capybara, have you?

Appendices

Effect of Climate Change on *Hydrochoerus hydrochaeris*
by Stacy Thomas Winnick and Prince Dobby Winnick
February 14, 2010

Department of Research; Stacy's Funny Farm, Washington, U.S.A.

ABSTRACT:

The Ice Age of Seattle, December 2009, caused devastating habitat loss for capybara in the Puget Sound Region of Washington State. Prior to the Ice Age, Dobby Winnick had free access to his owner's bedroom, including the corner home office area, the stairway to the Wine Cellar where his potatoes are stored, and the entire kitchen. He even had supervised access to the living room (with the coveted Eames Chair and its tasty armrest) and occasionally lurked beneath the dining table where he could nibble on knees and shoelaces throughout the evening repast.

In this study, temperatures were correlated with behavior and the subsequent loss of indoor habitat. The trend toward devilish bad behavior became clear even with the introduction of variables such as the returning college student, medical regimens, and the unfortunate and very untimely demise of equipment crucial to maintenance of the habitat.

Dobby has since returned to his original angelic disposition, but he will have to earn his way back into the lost habitat by displaying perfect behavior, as defined by strict maternal standards.

INTRODUCTION

Dobby Winnick is a capybara, *Hydrochoerus hydrochaeris*, a large graminivorous rodent indigenous to South America, primarily the Amazon River Basin Region. He was born in the United States of America (Texas) on Valentine's Day 2009, to Bonnie and Clyde Capybara. He was adopted by Stacy Winnick and moved to the Puget Sound Region of Washington State in early March, 2009, where he currently resides. He arrived in the Pacific Northwest to sub-freezing temperatures.

By the time he was old enough to spend extended time outdoors, typical dreary gray skies and constant drizzle had set in. Summer brought record-breaking heat to briefly scorch the soggy, moss covered mud in Dobby's yard. Autumn was unusually damp, and then December's Ice Age arrived.

As outdoor temperatures dropped below Dobby's comfort level, his indoor habitat became more and more restricted and degraded and his normally angelic indoor behavior deteriorated in response to the outdoor temperature. This study correlates the temperature changes and subsequent indoor habitat loss and degradation with Dobby's exhibited behavior.

MATERIALS AND METHODS

Several independent lines of data were collected during the month of December 2009, when the recent Ice Age occurred. A timeline of activities related to temperature and behavior was recorded. Temperature data was collected from a readily available online source. Habitat loss was tracked and recorded. Finally, Dobby's behavior was assessed using quantitative and qualitative criteria.

Dobby's pre-Ice Age indoor habitat consisted of several rooms, with both hardwood and carpeted flooring. As his behavior deteriorated, the areas Dobby considered to be the most desirable (carpeted- his tootsies slide like the devil on slick surfaces due to his exaggerated toenails) were transferred to the "What The Poop!," "Get the Heck Out of There," and/or "What Have You Done!" habitat category.

All of Dobby's carpeted indoor habitat was eventually transferred to one of these categories. Once he was confined to inferior habitat (hardwood floors, slick as snot), this area became degraded as area carpets were removed and even the ubiquitous IKEA Rabbit Rug ("Gosingen") was removed from service: it became too filthy for indoor use,

1

and yet remained too precious for outdoor use. Dobby eventually adapted to his new indoor habitat once the Rabbit Rug was returned to service.

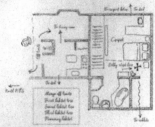

Figure 1 Indoor Habitat Loss

KEY QUANTITATIVE RESULTS

Nov. 30, 2009 Veterinary appointment: Dobby was taken to the veterinarian in an attempt to diagnose worms that were expelled in his urine. Symptoms include increased frequency of anal marking. Weight 58.3#, worm samples delivered, first Ivermectin injection: Ouch!

Dec. 1, 2009 First night of freezing weather: Dobby's outdoor pen is protected from inclement weather but only partially protected from the cold. He has an antique iron bed, several vintage blankets, a comforter, a small stuffed gray rabbit toy, and a heat lamp.

Dec. 6, 2009 23F degrees at night: And we discover that Dobby looks a bit funky in the morning. We resolve to let him sleep inside if the cold weather continues, though he has been known to soil his outdoor bedding on a nightly basis for the past 5 months.

Dec. 7, 2009 Temperatures continue to drop: Dobby moves indoors at bedtime and a shower curtain is placed under bedding to protect the carpet where he sleeps near the head of the Farm Manager's bed. It's really slippery. Bedding laundered.

Dec. 8, 2009 12F degrees at night, not much above freezing during the day. Dobby remains indoors much of the day. Anal marking continues, and carpeted east end of master bedroom is designated Off Limits. Bedding laundered.

Dec. 9, 2009 12F degrees at night, not much above freezing during the day. Dobby remains indoors much of the day. Anal marking continues, and large blankets are spread in bedroom area in an attempt to deter anal marking (ineffective). Bedding laundered.

Dec. 10, 2009 Still fricking cold, night and day: Second veterinary appointment, weight 60.2#, one more worm sample delivered, second Ivermectin injection. No diagnosis from Washington State parasitology lab. Fenbendazole prescribed as a precaution. Dobby is still sleeping indoors. Bedding laundered.

Dec. 11, 2009 Cold weather not yet ready to give in: Veterinarian calls with lab results. Dobby has a urinary tract infection. enrofloxacin (1-3/4) tablets daily, in milk, w/sugar to make the medicine go down. Dobby doesn't like this. Bedding laundered but the dryer is not working. We go out to an evening soiree, during which Dobby decorates the halls with 9 anal markings, 10 huge puddles of joy, and 11 piping piles of poo, through which one very angry lad has leaped, spreading holiday cheer. No hope for drying bedding and our stock of clean "sacrifice" blankets is diminishing. Wash everything anyway and start hanging it all around the house.

Dec. 12, 2009 This weather sucks: Pair of underpants, a shoebox of lint, and half gallon of water(?) is removed from dryer vent, and the dryer is ready for business! Washer dies unexpectedly, and diagnosis is grim. Merde. Bedding *not* laundered.

Dec. 13, 2009 I cannot believe this weather! Where is our rain? Bought new space-age heavy-duty washer from Sears Scratch-and-Dent, to be delivered "tomorrow".

2

173

Dec. 14, 2009 Ditto the weather, washer, dryer, Dobby's little surprises, which are now like diarrhea, thanks to the antibiotic that is killing his gut flora.

Dec. 15, 2009 Ditto the weather, washer, dryer: Human sister is home from college-watch your step!

Dec. 16, 2009 Ditto the weather, washer, dryer, Dobby's little surprises: Depth of ice on swimming pool reaches 6"

Dec. 17, 2009 Night temperatures are predicted to stay above freezing: Dobby moves back outside for bedtime!!! But he is still inside a lot of the day. It is not very nice outdoors.

Dec. 18, 2009 Weather continues to improve while multiplying dirty piles of laundry now decorate the halls. New washer arrives, promptly dies as the delivery van backs out the driveway and heads off down the street.

Dec. 19, 2009 Dobby moves outdoors for daytime: Do you hear that sigh of relief?

Dec. 20, 2009 Dobby's (now filthy) rabbit is removed from service

Dec. 21, 2009 Second new washer arrives, and amazes us all with its darling messages, sleek styling, *enormous* capacity, and nearly silent operation. Silent and constant.

Dec. 22, 2009 Dobby's spanking clean white rabbit rug returned to service

Dec. 23, 2009 Dobby starts probiotics, now that the antibiotics have reamed out his system.

Dec. 24, 2009 Enrofloxacin regimen complete but Dobby is now banished from the bedroom, even though we can now clean the blankets. Enough is enough.

Dec. 25, 2009 Dobby is now banished from the carpeted stairway. Temporary kitchen area set aside for Dobby.

Dec. 26, 2009 Dobby adapted to his kitchen area, somewhat. Temporary barriers reinforced after he barges past the hamster cage to decorate a previously untouched oriental carpet in the dining room.

Dec. 27, 2009 Dobby continues to adapt to the kitchen enclosure

Dec. 28, 2009 Dobby continues to adapt to the kitchen enclosure

Dec. 29, 2009 Dobby continues to adapt to the kitchen enclosure

Dec. 30, 2009 Dobby continues to adapt to the kitchen enclosure and starts *Eeeeep*ing! again. We hadn't really noticed when the *eep*s went away, but they are back.

Dec. 31, 2009 Ice on swimming pool melted. Happy New Year!

HIGH AND LOW TEMPERATURES

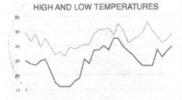

Figure 2 Outdoor Temperatures

Daily minimum and maximum outdoor temperatures are noted. Indoor temperatures ranged from 60.4F to 70.2F degrees and are not noted because this variable remained unchanged for the duration of the study.

3

SUPPLEMENTARY DATA

NOTE: From NOAA, the following commentary:

"The coldest temperatures of the year occurred in early December despite the sunshine and lack of snow on the ground. A number of daily record lows fell around the region including three consecutive days of 6 above zero at Olympia on the 8th...9th and 10th.

Dec 4-13 Western Washington

A cold snap gripped the region with the coldest temperatures of the year. A number of record low temperatures fell. Olympia dropped to 6 degrees above on Dec 8...9 and 10...the coldest this decade. Though damage results from the cold spell were not available yet...one local insurance company described the event as one of the top 6 severe cold weather events in the last 25 years with $4.3 million in claims."

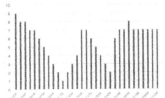

BEHAVIORAL ASSESSMENT

Figure 8 Devil or Angel

Dobby's behavior was rated on a scale from Angel through Devil on a daily basis throughout the Ice Age. His behavior correlates positively with the Key Quantitative Results, above.

INTERPRETATION OF THE DATA

Poor ickle Dobbykins didn't understand what happened to his lovely warm world. Everything got cold and then he got sick, but then he got to sleep inside again! That was like when he was a baby, but Big Boys don't go potty inside. But wait--it was fricking freezing cold outside, and there was no way he was going to go out there, no siree Bob! So, Dobby got pissed off and apparently he got pooped off, too. And then he got kicked outside again at night, when he thought things were going his way, and that pissed him off, too. Then his rabbit disappeared and didn't come back until the new washer came. For crying out loud, give him his cotton picking rabbit back!

Dobby is currently restricted to a generous play area in the kitchen, and is learning to ring a little bell to go outside when he needs to. Spare white rabbit rugs have been purchased for emergency use.

The worms. They turned out to be ejaculate. Oh, Dobby.

WORKS CITED

MesoWest Lake Forest Park Towne Center WA US WAAQ, Seattle, Washington (PWS), Weather History for This Location, 31 Dec. 2009, <http://www.wunderground.com>

National Weather Service Forecast Office. Seattle, WA, http://www.nws.noaa.gov

Winnick, Stacy. "Dobby and his White Rabbit Rug", "Two Toy Rabbits",

Hippopotatomus Channel, 29 December 2009, http://www.youtube.com/user/hippopotatomus

GLOSSARY

accoutrements, accessories, like fancy belt buckles

anaconda, a great big people eating snake, also a cult movie classic

anus, butt hole, poop comes from here

capybara, the world's most magnificent rodent

carnivore, animal that eats meat

cayman, a smallish South American crocodile

consequently, as a result

coprophages, edible portion of poop

Dag Nabbit, a famous 19th century diplomat

detritus, chunks of junk

Doofus Dance, a Dobby binky, a brief spasm of silliness

drake, a boy duck

dremel, toenail grinding tool

Eames Chair, like a baseball mitt you can sit in

freeboard, distance from the waterline to the overflow

graminivore, animal who eats grass

grim reaper, an impatient body snatcher

harpy eagle, gigantic South American eagle

herbivore, animal that eats vegetables

hiney, booty or tuchis

indisposed, not feeling too hot

interstitial, the spaces in between the stitials

introspection, taking a look inside yourself

jaguar, not the car, you dummy

jeepers creepers, eyeballs

jiminy cricket, formally attired insect

jumpin jehosephat, a perfectly useless exclamation

morrillo, marking scent gland on top of my snout

nuts, the neighborhood squirrels request an increased ration of peanuts

paragon, a shining example of excellence

persnickety, precise and particular, to be a stickler

piloerection, when my fur sticks out, like goosebumps with big hairs

piranha, carnivorous fish

pneumonia, a serious lung infection

pouffy, like puffy or poufy but even fluffier

prerogative, privilege due to rank

probiotic, food for your gut flora to help digestion

radiograph, the pictures that are taken using x-rays

rodent, mammals that have great big front teeth that grow constantly

ROUS, Rodent of Unusual Size (from movie *The Princess Bride*)

ROUS Foundation, support fundraising group to the R.O.U.S. Fund

R.O.U.S. Fund, Texas A&M University non-profit organization benefiting capybara health

rumblestrut, guinea pig boars impress the sows with this swagger

schnozzola, big fat nose

skoshe, just a tad

skedaddle, get away with a jack rabbit start

sugar gliders, small cranky squirrel-like flying marsupials

tuchis, your bottom

upcycled, recycled into something better than its original purpose

voilà, here it is, as if by magic!

what in tarnation? see what in the sam hill, below

what in the sam hill? Sam Hill built the roads that connected Eastern Washington to the Coast in the early 1900's. His estate, now an art museum located in Maryhill, WA (named after his daughter). Many thought he was crazy for thinking the roads could be engineered and completed. The use of his name when planning a task or acting in a way that is considered crazy or impossible.

verboten, forbidden in Germany

willy nilly, not what it sounds like

X-ray, roentgen ray

WHERE CAN YOU SEE CAPYBARAS?

It's shocking, I know, but outside of South America, most capybaras live in zoos. It's really the best place to see us because according to the ROUS Foundation, there are fewer than a hundred pet capybaras worldwide. Most are even more private than I am. Even though the Farm Manager can look at a capybara in her kitchen, she went to Brazil and Panama to see capybaras in the wild. It's so much easier to see us at a zoo. Sometimes you can even see us in small petting zoos. If you're in Japan, all of the zoos seem to have capys. Japanese capybara exhibits all have hot tubs, spas, and massage parlors. I'm not kidding.

The Farm Manager has been compiling this list of zoos for several years, but the only way to be certain the zoo near you has capybaras is to phone them. Websites are not always up to date, and of course, this list will become obsolete the moment this book goes to print. Let the reader beware! I will continue to update the Zoo Project on my website. With your valuable input, we can keep the online list up-to-date!

United States

AL	Montgomery Zoo	http://www.montgomeryzoo.com/
AR	Little Rock Zoo	http://www.littlerockzoo.com/
AZ	Out of Africa Wildlife Park, Camp Verde	http://outofafricapark.com/
AZ	Reid Park Zoo, Tucson	https://reidparkzoo.org/
AZ	Wildlife World Zoo & Aquarium, Litchfield Park	http://www.wildlifeworld.com/
CA	Fresno Chaffee Zoo, Fresno	http://www.fresnochaffeezoo.org/
CA	Happy Hollow Zoo, San Jose	http://www.hhpz.org/
CA	San Diego Zoo	http://www.sandiegozoo.org/

CA	San Francisco Zoo http://www.sfzoo.org/
CO	Denver Zoological Gardens http://www.denverzoo.org/
DE	Brandywine Zoo, Wilmington https://brandywinezoo.org/
FL	Brevard Zoo, Melbourne https://brevardzoo.org/
FL	Jacksonville Zoo http://www.jacksonvillezoo.org/
FL	Palm Beach Zoo and Conservation Society, West Palm Beach http://www.palmbeachzoo.org/
FL	Zooworld, Panama City Beach http://zooworldpcb.com/
ID	Zoo Boise, Boise https://zooboise.org/
IL	Scovill Children's Zoo, Decatur http://www.decatur-parks.org/scovill-zoo/
KS	Rolling Hills Zoo, Salina http://www.rollinghillszoo.org/
KS	Sedgwick County Zoo, Wichita https://www.scz.org/
LA	Alexandria Zoo, Alexandria http://www.thealexandriazoo.com/
LA	Audubon Nature Institute, New Orleans http://audubonnatureinstitute.org/zoo
LA	Baton Rouge Zoo http://www.brzoo.org/
MA	Forest Park Zoo, Springfield https://www.forestparkzoo.org/
MA	Franklin Park Zoo/Stone Zoo, Boston http://www.zoonewengland.org/franklin-park-zoo
MA	Southwick's Zoo, Menden http://southwickszoo.com/
MD	Salisbury Zoological Park, Salisbury http://www.salisburyzoo.org/

ME	York's Wild Kingdom, York http://www.yorkswildkingdom.com/
MI	Detroit Zoological Society, Royal Oak https://detroitzoo.org/
MI	John Ball Zoo, Grand Rapids http://www.jbzoo.org/
MO	Kansas City Zoo, Kansas City https://www.kansascityzoo.org/
MO	Saint Louis Zoological Park https://www.stlzoo.org/
MS	Hattiesburg Zoo http://www.zoohattiesburg.com/
NJ	Bergen County Zoological Park, Paramus http://www.co.bergen.nj.us/437/Bergen-County-Zoo
NJ	Cape May County Park Zoo http://www.cmczoo.com/
NJ	Turtle Back Zoo, West Orange http://turtlebackzoo.com/
NM	Albuquerque Biological Park http://www.cabq.gov/culturalservices/biopark/zoo
NY	Animal Adventure Park, Harpursville http://theanimaladventurepark.com/
NY	Buffalo Zoological Gardens https://buffalozoo.org/
NY	Staten Island Zoo http://www.statenislandzoo.org/
OH	African Safari Wildlife Park, Port Clinton http://www.africansafariwildlifepark.com/
OH	Akron Zoological Park, Akron http://www.akronzoo.org/
OH	Cincinnati Zoo & Botanical Garden http://cincinnatizoo.org/
OH	Cleveland Metroparks Zoo https://www.clevelandmetroparks.com/zoo
OR	West Coast Game Park, Bandon http://www.westcoastgameparksafari.com/

PA	Elmwood Park Zoo, Norristown
	http://www.elmwoodparkzoo.org/
PA	Erie Zoo
	https://www.eriezoo.org/
PA	Lake Tobias Zoo, Halifax
	https://www.laketobias.com/
PA	Pittsburgh Zoo & PPG Aquarium
	http://www.pittsburghzoo.org/
SC	Waccatee Zoological Farm, Myrtle Beach
	http://www.waccateezoo.com/
TN	Brights Zoo, Limestone
	http://www.brightszoo.com/
TN	Chattanooga Zoo
	http://www.chattzoo.org/
TN	Memphis Zoo
	https://www.memphiszoo.org/
TX	Caldwell Zoo, Tyler
	http://caldwellzoo.org/
TX	Cameron Park Zoo, Waco
	http://www.cameronparkzoo.com/
TX	Dallas World Aquarium
	http://www.dwazoo.com/
TX	Dallas Zoo
	http://www.dallaszoo.com/
TX	El Paso Zoo
	http://www.elpasozoo.org/
TX	Gladys Porter Zoo, Brownsville
	http://gpz.org/
TX	Houston Zoo
	http://www.houstonzoo.org/
TX	San Antonio Zoological Gardens and Aquarium
	https://sazoo.org/
TX	Sharkarosa Park, Pilot Point
	https://www.sharkarosa.com/
TX	Snake Farm, New Braunfels
	http://www.awsfzoo.com/

TX	TDS Game Ranch, Creedmore http://www.texasdisposal.com/exotic-game-ranch/
VA	Roer's Zoofari, Reston http://www.roerszoofari.com/
WI	Henry Vilas Zoo, Madison http://www.vilaszoo.org/

Canada

Alberta	Edmonton Valley Zoo, Edmonton https://www.edmonton.ca/attractions_events/ edmonton-valley-zoo.aspx
B.C.	Aldergrove Zoo, Vancouver http://gvzoo.com/
B.C.	Kangaroo Creek Farm, Winfield http://kangaroocreekfarm.com/
Ontario	Bervie Zoological Park, Kincardine https://www.facebook.com/Bervie-Zoological- Park-483709711689878/
Ontario	Riverview Park and Zoo, Peterborough http://www.peterboroughutilities.ca/Park_and_Zoo.htm
Ontario	Toronto Zoo, Scarborough http://www.torontozoo.com/
Ontario	High Park Zoo, Toronto https://www.highparkzoo.ca/
Ontario	Bowmanville Zoo, Toronto http://www.bowmanvillezoo.com/
Quebec	Biodome, Montreal http://ville.montreal.qc.ca/
Quebec	Granby Zoo, Granby https://zoodegranby.com/en/

Europe

Austria	Vienna Zoo (Tiergarten Schonbrunn) http://www.zoovienna.at/
Belgium	Dierenpark Planckendael, Mechelem https://www.planckendael.be/en/

Belarus	Minsk Zoo http://minskzoo.by/en/	
Czech Republic		
	Zoological Garden in Jihlava (Zoologická Zahrada Jihlava) http://www.zoojihlava.cz/en/	
Denmark	Copenhagen http://www.zoo.dk/	
England	Birmingham Wildlife Conservation Park https://www.birmingham.gov.uk/bhamconservationpark	
England	Chessington Zoo, Surrey https://www.chessington.com/explore/chessington-zoo/	
England	Chester Zoo, Upton-by-Chester http://www.chesterzoo.org/	
England	Combe Martin Wildlife and Dinosaur Park, Ilfracombe http://www.wildlifedinosaurpark.co.uk/	
England	Cotswold Wildlife Park & Gardens, Bradwell Grove, Burford, Oxfordshire http://www.cotswoldwildlifepark.co.uk/	
England	Dartmoor Zoological Park, Sparkwell, Plymouth, Devon http://www.dartmoorzoo.org.uk/	
England	Drusillas Park, Alfriston, East Sussex http://www.drusillas.co.uk/	
England	Exmoor Zoo, South Stowford, Bratton Fleming, Barnstaple, North Devon http://www.exmoorzoo.co.uk/	
England	Port Lympne Reserve, Nr. Ashford, Kent https://www.aspinallfoundation.org/port-lympne/	
England	Newquay Zoo, Trenance Gardens, Newquay, Cornwall http://www.newquayzoo.org.uk/	
England	Peak Wildlife Park, Winkhill, Leek http://www.peakwildlifepark.co.uk/	
England	Safari Zoo, Melton Terrace, Lindal-in-Furness, Ulverston, Cumbria https://www.southlakessafarizoo.com/	
England	Twycross Zoo, Burton Road, Atherstone, Warwickshire https://twycrosszoo.org/	

Germany	Zoo Schwerin, Germany http://www.zoo-schwerin.de/	
Germany	Erlebnis Zoo, Hannover, Germany https://www.zoo-hannover.de/de	
Germany	Tierpark Chemnitz, Chemnitz, Germany http://www.tierpark-chemnitz.de/	
Holland	Burgers' Zoo, Arnhem, The Netherlands https://www.burgerszoo.com/	
Holland	Apenheul Primate Park, Apeldoorn, The Netherlands https://www.apenheul.nl/	
Holland	Artis Zoo, Amsterdam, The Netherlands https://www.artis.nl/nl/	
Hungary	Budapest Zoo and Botanical Garden, Hungary http://www.zoobudapest.com/	
Ireland	Fota Island Wildlife Park, Ireland http://www.fotawildlife.ie/	

Northern Ireland

Belfast Zoo
http://www.belfastzoo.co.uk/

Russia

Russia	Krasnoyarsk Park of Flora and Fauna https://roev.ru/	
Russia	Moscow Zoo, Russia http://moscowzoo.su/	
Russia	Limpopo Zoo, Yaroshenko http://www.nnzoo.ru/	
Russia	Novosibirsk Zoo http://zoonovosib.ru/	
Russia	Perm Zoo http://www.zoo.perm.ru/	
Russia	Rostov-on-Don Zoo, Rostov http://www.zoopark-rostov.ru/	
Slovakia	Zoo Bratislava http://www.zoobratislava.sk/	

Slovenia	Ljubljana Zoo, Slovenia http://www.zoo.si/
Spain	Barcelona Zoo, Spain http://www.zoobarcelona.cat/
Sweden	Kolmarden Animal Park, Norrkoping http://www.kolmarden.com/
Sweden	Parken Zoo, Eskiltuna http://www.parkenzoo.se/
Switzerland	Berne Animal Park, Berne, Switzerland http://www.tierpark-bern.ch/
Switzerland	Zurich Zoo , Switzerland http://www.zoo.ch/
Ukraine	Kiev Zoo http://zoo.kiev.ua/
Ukraine	Rivne Zoo http://zoopark.rv.ua/
Wales	Folly Farm, Begelly, Kilgetty, Pembrokeshire https://www.folly-farm.co.uk/zoo

Latin America

Bolivia	Santa Cruz Zoo, Bolivia http://www.boliviabella.com/santa-cruz-zoo.html
Brazil	Bosque dos Jequitibas, Campinas, Sao Paulo http://www.campinas.sp.gov.br/sobre-campinas/ atracoes-naturais.php
Brazil	Rio Zoo, Rio de Janeiro http://riozoo.com.br/
Brazil	Jardim Zoologico de Sao Paulo http://www.zoologico.com.br/
Mexico	Chapultepec Zoo, Mexico City http://data.sedema.cdmx.gob.mx/zoo_chapultepec/
Uruguay	Eco-Zoologico Reserve, Baños de Agua Santa http://ecozoosanmartin.com/

Asia

Hong Kong	Ocean Park https://www.oceanpark.com.hk/en

Japan	Izu Shaboten Zoological Park (Izu Cactus Park), Ito http://capybara.eek.jp/navi-sabo.html
Japan	Nagasaki Bio Park http://www.biopark.co.jp/en/
Japan	Nasu Animal Kingdom, Nasu-machi http://www.nasu-oukoku.com/
Japan	Saitama Children's Zoo http://www.parks.or.jp/sczoo/
Japan	*Many other zoos in Japan feature capybaras:* http://capybara.eek.jp/navi.html
Malaysia	Zoo Negara, Malaysia http://www.zoonegaramalaysia.my/
Singapore	Night Safari of Singapore http://www.nightsafari.com.sg/
Taiwan	Taipei Zoo, Taiwan http://www.zoo.gov.taipei/

Elsewhere

Antilles	St. Maarten Zoo, Philipsburg, St. Maarten, Netherlands Antilles http://www.stmaartenzoo.com/
Australia	Adelaide Zoo, South Australia https://www.adelaidezoo.com.au/
Australia	Wildlife HQ Zoo, Queensland https://whqzoo.com/
Bahamas	Ardastra Gardens, Zoo & Conservation Centre, Nassau http://www.ardastra.com/
South Africa	Joburg Zoo, Johannesburg, South Africa http://www.jhbzoo.org.za/
Trinidad	Emperor Valley Zoo, Port of Spain, Trinidad http://www.zstt.org/

OTHER CAPYBARA RESOURCES

Find me on the Internet

Dobby's own website https://petcapybara.com/

Dobby's Facebook page https://www.facebook.com/dobbywinnick/

Dobby's YouTube channel https://www.youtube.com/user/hippopotatomus

Dobby's Twitter handle @hippopotatomus at https://twitter.com/hippopotatomus

Instagram https://www.instagram.com/stacysfunnyfarm

Pinterest https://www.pinterest.com/hippopotatomus

Stacy's Funny Farm https://stacysfunnyfarm.wordpress.com

Tumblr http://hippopotatomus.tumblr.com/

Zazzle https://www.zazzle.com/stacys+funny+farm+gifts

Capybara themed websites and other good stuff

Capybara Madness http://gianthamster.com/

Funny Foot Farm https://www.facebook.com/fuzzybottomblog/

The Capybara Page http://www.rebsig.com/capybara

ROUS Foundation http://rousfoundation.com

R.O.U.S. Fund at Texas A&M University http://vetmed.tamu.edu/giving/opportunities/rous

Dobby's 2016 presidential campaign http://www.newyorker.com/magazine/2016/09/05/hillary-clinton-and-donald-trumps-latest-polls

Consider adding these books to your capybara collection

Lord, Rexford D.; *Capybaras: A Natural History of the World's Largest Rodent;* The Johns Hopkins University Press; Maryland, 2009.

Moreira, José Roberto, Ferraz, Katia Maria P.M.B., Hererra, Emilio A., Macdonald, and David W.; *Capybara: Biology, Use and Conservation of an Exceptional Neotropical Species;* Springer; New York, 2003.

Peet, Bill; *Capyboppy;* HMH Books for Young Readers; 1985.

Plus over 20 children's picture books. Check your local library.

Other books about animals that I like

Grandin, Temple; *Animals in Translation;* Harcourt, 2006.

Lombardi, Linda; *Animals Behaving Badly;* Perigree Books, 2011.

O'Brien, Stacey; *Wesley the Owl;* Atria Books, 2009.

Stanger, Margaret A.; *That Quail, Robert;* J. B. Lippincott Company, 1966.

Tarte, Bob; *Enslaved by Ducks;* Algonquin Press, 2004.

ACKNOWLEDGEMENTS

I hesitate to admit that I had any help at all with this manuscript. By hiding acknowledgements, way back here, only the people who are mentioned will bother looking for it. As royalty, I am not expected to give thanks, nor does my staff care one fig about such things. However, the follow-up novel is proving to be a greater challenge, mostly due to the liability I am incurring by incorporating so many of them into the story. As a preemptive strike against future litigation, it seems prudent for me to sing their praises at this juncture. For those who have already been offended by this work, please contact my attorney. She is the more aggressive of the two Wistar rats in the tower suite of the guinea pig room.

I suppose I should thank Dick (The Bartender) for the excellent cuisine, served promptly if without flair. Truth be known, he is more butler to me than bartender, that role intended to mollify the long-suffering Farm Manager. The Bartender is at once the chauffeur, the supply Sargent, the charwoman, and emergency wrangler. My hat is off to you, sir.[54]

My human brother saw me through the lean years, my babyish antics, my complete and total abduction of the Farm Manager. All attention flowed to me and I do not fault you for leaving this palace as my claim to royalty became apparent. As one mature male to another, I accept your deference, but when you visit do not overstay your welcome. Your lovely cohort, however, is welcome to stay if she wishes.

Many thanks to my adoring human sister, with whom I have inadvertently scuffled. You now know how I adore you, and I hope I never need to bite you again. Will you ever forgive me? I hereby entreat you to return, take the princess suite, stay as long as you like. I will nibble your fingers, that's all, I promise! And, by the way, thanks for all of your help with the Kickstarter!

---

54 Make me wear a hat and you will pay for it with your life.

My incomparable support staff is indispensable! Kannon was first on board, crafting my kitchen area and then my lavatory. Connor was up next, wrangler extraordinaire and all around devotee to all things in and around this palace. Jillian was a consistent presence for many years but I fear she was too much enamored with the guinea pigs to deal with brutes like me. Such is the life of royalty: we don't always receive the adoration we deserve. Puppy Dreams pet sitting facilitated random abandonments by their exemplary service. And then there are the neighbors who put up with my intermittent and half-hearted barking and yes, braying. It's nothing compared to Norman's honking, but it all adds up.

Reluctantly, I would like to acknowledge Sears repair service, for their diligence and indulgence. Maybe they never noticed the blog posts featuring their service representatives, but I am grateful that no lawsuits resulted from the dubious publicity.

My veterinarian, Dr. F, is a courageous and exceptionally talented practitioner, and his former cohort, Dr. M, is spunky if not thrilled with the bite holes I chewed in the chairs of her clinic. Dr. S, encouraged by Melanie and the ROUS Foundation, is amassing capybara veterinary data to benefit all veterinarians facing capybara diagnoses. Mary Lee, capybara creator extraordinaire, is aware of her role in this adventure. The entire capybara community is indebted to her for the wealth of care and breeding information she has both acquired and distributed over many years. Rick and Abby, your little capybara is quite a scamp!

Without Sonya, most of you would be utterly oblivious regarding my stunning attractiveness. Not only did she draw every picture in this book, her complete faith in my ability to overcome obstacles (such as typing with big clumsy paws) startled me into completing this important work. I dared not leave her holding a fistful of capybara drawings with no text to explain them.

My Beta, Charlie, and Delta readers and reviewers—Jennifer, Susan, Melanie, Ella, Jan, Pam, Marti, Jeanne, and (the one and only) Dick—simultaneously encouraged and discouraged me from the horrors inflicted upon them by a novice writer. It may be hard to believe, but the original document rambled, contradicted, and assaulted the reader to a much greater degree than this final effort. Thanks, everybody.

Then there was Linda, who started this zoo nonsense, and Georgi, who provided evidentiary documents indicating we were on the right track. I'll tell you a secret: that isn't my voice on the Kickstarter video. It's multi-talented Georgi! Mr. P's 6th grade students taught me how to tell my story by listening to the best parts and fidgeting for the rest. My Facebook fans asked me to tell my story, and I hope they don't regret it. I am certain to hear about it if they do! Detonator Beth, who secretly included me on her bucket list, checked me off, and left the stage: I am honored to have brought you a joyous afternoon. Finally, I wish to thank Jeff for his word of encouragement.

AUTHOR BIOGRAPHY

Dobby the Capybara is currently employed as the Director of Fundraising for Stacy's Funny Farm, a non-profit small pet sanctuary.

Stacy Winnick, the Farm Manager, has been wrangling rodents since 1952. Beginning with hamsters and working her way up, her relationship with Dobby became complicated in 2009. Stacy has been an integral member of the obscure capybara community since Dobby first marked her oriental carpets. As Vice President of the ROUS Foundation, her dubious advice is sought by capybara owners worldwide. She has observed wild capybaras in Panama and Brazil. At home, she can be found wandering aimlessly among her admirers, mostly ducks and hens.

ABOUT STACY'S FUNNY FARM

Stacy's Funny Farm is a small non-profit pet sanctuary providing live out full term care (LOFT) for assorted homeless pets.

ILLUSTRATOR BIOGRAPHY

Sonya Reasor has been drawing Dobby forever. She has photographed every inch of her garden and cat, exploring the outdoors if the rain stops long enough. She asked me not to divulge her passion for skulls, or mention her dodgy collection. She even asked Dobby to be the ring bearer at her wedding, but she forgot about his unfortunate marking habits. In real life, she works as a graphic designer and illustrator.